OLD TIME RAILROAD STORIES

*An Anthology of True Adventures,
Humorous Tales, and High Melodrama
Written by Those Who Lived the Era*

EDITED, WITH INTRODUCTIONS
BY MICHAEL GILLESPIE

Published by
  Great River Publishing
  W987 Cedar Valley Road
  Stoddard, WI 54658
  608-457-2734

On the Internet, please visit www.greatriver.com

ISBN 978-0-9711602-5-5

First Edition
Designed by Sue Knopf, Graffolio, La Crosse, Wisconsin

Printed in the United States of America

Permissions
Photos courtesy Library of Congress unless otherwise noted.

Dedicated to the memory of my father,
Leo M. Gillespie
(1918-1999)

He was, in turn, a farmer, a pilot, and a
steelworker.
*But he always **wanted** to be a railroad engineer.*

Other books by Michael Gillespie,
published by Great River Publishing (Heritage Press)

Come Hell or High Water
A Lively History of Steamboating
on the Mississippi and Ohio Rivers
ISBN 978-0-9620823-2-0

Wild River, Wooden Boats
True Stories of Steamboating and the Missouri River
ISBN 978-0-9620823-7-5

CONTENTS

Preface vii

A Cab Ride on the Limited 1
Anonymous

He Kept His Word 9
J. A. Allard

The Girl Operator 15
Anonymous

The Tallow-Pot's Tale 39
Charles W. Tyler

An Obstinate Farmer 55
The New York Times

High Speed Johnnie 57
W.H. Henry

Asleep on Duty 61
Anonymous

Night of the Wolves 67
Angus Sinclair

A Novel Battle 75
Cy Warman

The Superintendent and Pawnee Bill 85
S.T. Sallee

Only a Switchman   88
Tony Eckart

When the Texan Was Yardmaster   95
E.W. Swan

The Lap Order   107
Frederick A. Starges

The Night Dispatcher   115
Frank L. Packard

The Holdup of No. 8   133
F.R. Dresbach

Glossary   141

About the Author   159

Now Available from Great River Publishing   161

PREFACE

There was a time when nothing moved faster than a train. It was the era of the railroad, which, give or take a decade, lasted from the 1870s through the 1910s. In those faded times the arrival of the daily passenger train was the high point of most any day in small-town America. It was a time, too, when just about every farm boy within earshot of a fast moving freight yearned to escape the plow and ride to fame and glory as an engineer or brakeman.

Nor was this fascination limited to a rustic few. Fledgling authors found it a field ripe with possibilities. Here was action and adventure waiting to be written—tragedy, melodrama, comic relief—all wrapped up in the swirling, swaying rush of a passing train. The pulp market of the day eagerly published prose or pondering—fact or fiction—about the railroad. And even the literary magazines deemed the subject to be worthy of occasional attention.

The period in which these tales were written was a seminal time for the railroad industry. The late-nineteenth, early-twentieth century period marked a significant era of transition. The era began with a strong belief that no form of transportation could possibly replace the railroad—it was thought to be the ultimate means of moving people and goods, and would grow more or less continually. In contrast, waterborne transportation was limited to a relatively small corridor and was subject, in all but the lower latitudes, to seasonal limitations. Land transportation, via the existing roadway network, also was subject to the whims of climate. Too, there was an inherent limitation to roadway transportation, for a team of draft animals could pull only a fraction of the tonnage assigned to a typical railroad train. And what else was there? Steam tractors? Airships? These hardly seemed practical. Only the automobile could challenge the railroad industry. But the coming age of the automobile, though poised to make a monumental change in the American way of moving people and things, had not yet fully developed when the last of our stories was penned.

The era here encountered also saw a great deal of transition in the purely technical aspects of railroading. In the 1890s Congress passed the Railroad Safety Appliance Act. This mandated the use of automatic couplers, as opposed to the simple yet dangerous link-and-pin system. The link-and-pin probably contributed to more injuries and deaths on the railroad than any other device in common use. The act also required the installation of a braking system whereby the engineer could stop his train from the cab. This, in essence, meant equipping most cars with air brakes. Another part of the law called for grab irons to be placed on the ends and sides of the cars. These contrivances, as obviously necessary as they seem today, were by no means taken for granted at the dawn of the progressive era.

And yet some seemingly understandable changes did not make their way onto the railroad scene as quickly as one might expect. For instance, electric lights and steam heating on passenger cars were far from the norm when most of our tales were written. Dynamos for generating electricity throughout a train generally did not make the scene until after World War I; until then even the engine headlight was nothing more than a large lantern with a mirror reflector. Wood or coal burning stoves heated most passenger equipment, and were quite prone to set the cars on fire if they overturned in a wreck.

The hours of service laws did not come into being until 1907, and even then a sleep deprived railroad crewman could be compelled to work up to 16 hours in any 24-hour period. Prior to that, nothing could prevent a road from forcing an employee to work around the clock.

Unions, representing the various railroad crafts and trades, were still struggling to gain acceptance during the whole period. The railroad companies deemed unions to be anti-Capitalist, even subversive. Any railroad employee who joined a union did so at his own risk, for to go on strike was paramount to quitting one's job. Most rail union employees would pay their dues and hope, through some favorable legislation, to attain settlement for the many unaddressed grievances they held against their employers. Railroad union journals were the principal means of connection for this far-flung membership. Regular features in these publications included shop talk, legislative advances, lodge news, travelogues, notes of interest for wives, and some of the very stories found herein.

What follows is a gleaning of the school of railroad literature published during the height of the era. The stories are taken not only from the journals and magazines of the trade, but from the popular press of the day. All of these stories have some basis in fact, and in that regard they may be considered historically compelling.

The stories in this anthology, even the ones written as newspaper reports, were meant as entertainment, first and foremost. Whether they could be taken seriously or not mattered not so much as the fact that they amused the reader. That was their contemporary purpose, and no apologies for digressions from fact were expected, nor given. But across the chasm of time their purpose has changed. They are now as much a chronicle of their day as once they were an amusement—a folk history, if you will—coarse and incomplete, but tantalizing. For what they often lack in formality, they make up in human detail. They open a window to a pattern of life that is no more.

Some of the accounts have been edited. This was done either for considerations of length or clarity, especially when a more concise wording would better conform to the mind of the present-day reader. In either case, the edits were made with due consideration to the original intent of the author.

These old time railroad stories are tales of righteousness and morality set amidst the background of coal smoke and the incessant clatter of the telegraph sounder. Some may regard these narratives as musty remnants of a simpler time, but as the reader will see, they are full of life and emotion, and speak to each generation in ways that never change.

A Cab Ride on the Limited

The Twentieth Century Limited, circa 1905.

In 1902, the New York Central inaugurated its premier passenger train, the **Twentieth Century Limited**. *The* **Limited** *ran between New York and Chicago on a blistering 16-hour overnight run. It immediately captured the public's fancy and would continue to do so throughout the steam railroad era.*

In order to maintain its sixty mile per hour average speed, the Limited enjoyed superior rights over all other trains. It even drew water on the fly instead of stopping at water tanks. This astounding feat was accomplished by the use of a scoop that sucked up water from a long trough installed between the rails.

It's unknown how many newspaper correspondents got the opportunity to ride in the cab of the **Twentieth Century Limited**. *It obviously made good copy for the paper, and good publicity for the railroad, but it could be a harrowing ride for a reluctant reporter, as we are about to read, from 1905—* **The Twentieth Century Limited**, *circa 1905.*

Undoubtedly a conspiracy had been formed to prevent me from flunking. It had for its head W. C. Brown, vice-president of the Lake Shore and New York Central Railroad and extended on down the line through the general superintendent to the yardmaster at the Collingwood yards just out of Cleveland.

In an unguarded moment I had expressed a desire to take a night ride on a locomotive during a fast run.

"How would the Twentieth Century do?" asked the vice-president in his quick and snappy business tone.

"Bully," I replied in an offhand way, as though plunging through dense darkness at seventy miles an hour was my customary after dinner recreation.

"There, that will fix you; I mean it," declared Mr. Brown. "Here's your pass," as the boy who had been sent to C. F. Daly of the passenger department returned. "You take the train here in a half-hour, get a good lunch and then a fine dinner before you arrive at Cleveland, and eight miles out of there you get on the engine and ride to Buffalo."

I felt like a schoolboy caught at his pranks, but, swallowing a big lump, I hastened to the depot and crawled into a dark corner of a Pullman, thinking to escape detection. It was no use, for a man with brass buttons soon came along and thrust one of Mr. Brown's miserable telegrams in my hands. It read: "J. F. Dane, conductor train No. 26— Inform Mr. X, who is a passenger on your train, that arrangements have been made for him to ride on the engine from Collingwood to Buffalo."

"Do you have to do it?" asked Dane, a puzzled look on his face.

"If this keeps up I don't see how I can duck it," I replied gloomily.

Just as I would begin to sink into a feeling of security against detection another Mr. Brass Buttons would show up with another one of Brown's telegrams. To make matters worse, H. A. Ziessel, division superintendent at Chicago, began to work the wires overtime after we had passed Elkhart. Finally, as we approached Cleveland, the baggageman came in with a yellow message which read: "See that Mr. X is provided with a suit of jumpers, a cap, and a bandana handkerchief."

While I was being led into the baggage car and outfitted, the train pulled into the yards at Collingwood. There I entered the cab.

Jack Dollingshead, a somewhat diminutive fireman, gifted with Sandowic muscles, said I could sit ahead of him, the farther ahead the less chance I would have of being thrown out of the cab window. He also made a funnel of his hands and glued his mouth to my ear to inform me that we were twenty-six minutes late and there was likely to be "something doing." The lights of the Collingwood yard hadn't disappeared before that "something doing" appeared in the unexpected form of a cloudburst, which the papers said the next day was one of the worst in years.

In a trice there were three men in that cab who could not have been more drenched had they plunged into the Red Sea before the waters were parted. To make matters more delightful, the torrents of rain that struck the boiler head instantly turned to blinding steam, which sizzled and hissed like a thousand serpents and made "seein' things" at night impossible. In desperation, I crawled up behind the engineer, only to be struck in the back by a deluge of rain driven by a hurricane through the opposite gangway and window. Finally I landed in the center of the cab and stood there dancing an impromptu hornpipe as the big monster reeled and twisted and jumped with the impact of a 500-ton train being hurled through space at a sixty-mile clip.

By the time Dollingshead discovered that there was a nail under the window sash and had extracted the same, I was standing in a river of water in the steam room of an improvised Turkish bathhouse.

When I crept up in front of Dollingshead again and looked ahead it was into black, inky nothingness. I felt creepy. How was the ossified sphinx over on the right side of the cab to see the signals or the track? I asked the fireman if the operating rules did not call for reduced speed in such a storm.

"Not for the *Twentieth Century Limited* when she's behind time," screamed the little man of muscle.

"How do you do it?" I asked, thoroughly frightened as she heeled over on the off side of a two percent curve.

"Trust in luck and keep her going."

They kept her going all right, and I resolved that if luck favored me it would be the last time I would go farther forward than the rear Pullman. Soaked to the skin, I suddenly remembered that my doctor had told me that the one thing I must avoid at all hazards was wet feet.

"No matter where you are, or what you are doing," cautioned the doctor, "if you get wet feet don't keep 'em." So I off with my dripping shoes and elevated my feet on the hot boiler head and left them to dry out.

Dried out and the storm over, I began to take an interest in things. Having heard of track tanks and of taking water when going forty-five miles an hour, I wanted to see how it was done. Dollingshead motioned for me to get down on the cab floor and look steadily at two square holes in the forward tender plates over which iron doors swung loosely. When the water came rushing into the tank with the force of a battering-ram the doors flew outward and a second cloudburst occurred. Drenched to the skin again, but still wiser, I was compelled to repeat the drying-out process on the top of the boiler. Dollingshead apologized, but the grin on his face killed it for me.

Taking water on the fly from a track pan.

I had just gotten myself comfortably fixed when I felt a sudden sensation akin to the bottom falling out of everything. The fireman sprang to his perch, and confided to me that we had "dropped over the brow of Ripley Hill, and were off for a straight down shoot of twenty-one miles."

"We've had rotten luck," he shouted, "and are thirty minutes late. Just watch your Uncle William over there throw her down this hill."

"Who threw that brick?" I asked the fireman.

"Brick?" he laughed. "That was only the town of Van Kuren which we passed through."

"You'll have to show me if that thing flying at the cab was a town."

"You couldn't see it. We came down that hill twenty-one miles in thirteen minutes, better than ninety-six miles an hour."

Dollingshead was soon engaged in raking the fire, and as we swung around a sharp curve at the bottom of the hill there, not more than 1,000 feet ahead, was a fiend swinging a red lantern vigorously across the track. I remembered that a 500-ton train going above sixty miles an hour could not be stopped under 3,000 feet, and so I shut my eyes and waited, expecting not to open them again in this world. Wheelock made three moves simultaneously, reversing the lever, closing the throttle, and making an emergency application of air. From the sound behind us I was sure all five Pullmans and the baggage car were piling on top of the engine and tender.

Dollingshead had been unable to get the rake out, and applying the air with the fire door open operated like a ten-horsepower bellows on a fiery furnace. The cab instantly became filled with smoke and lurid flames, which leaped upon Dollingshead, burning his hair, eyebrows, and mustache, and one side of his face. My suit of jumpers also was burned merrily.

Grasping the hose, he turned it on me for the third cloudburst of the evening. Before my conflagration was put out and the rake gotten out of the firebox, we had shot past that red light, which, we discovered, was being swung for a train coming in the opposite direction.

Dollingshead rubbed oil on his burns, and glancing at the engineer ruefully, said: "Bill if you're not careful you'll burn someone up some time."

"Sorry, old man, but that light was pretty close."

"Aren't you going to dry out again?" asked the fireman as he crawled up behind me.

"What's the use?" I asked. "I understand there are more rivers between here and Buffalo."

My nerves were threatening to become settled again, when I sprang from the seat, bumping my head against the roof of the cab as two reports seemingly as loud as a cannon's were heard directly beneath the engine.

"Some one dynamite us?" I asked.

"Nope, torpedoes. That's a warning to look out for something in the block ahead."

"Why don't you do it?"

"Thirty-five minutes late."

"Bang," came a third report, and on went the emergency air again. This time we ran plumb up to the rear of a freight, stopping in front of a small telegraph station. Wheelock reached from the cab and grasped a yellow order which read "No. 72," that was the freight, "will run ahead of No. 26," that was us, "to Dunkirk."

A second order read: "No. 26 will pass No. 72 in the block at Dunkirk."

The engineer swore softly, and a fresh plug disappeared into his left cheek as he pulled the throttle and began crawling after No. 72. When we finally drew into the Buffalo yards, thirty-five minutes late, with my jumpers half burned off, my face as black as tar, and the constant roar as loud as a thousand thunderstorms in my head, I asked Wheelock: "Am I a hoodoo?"

"I'm not superstitious," he answered laconically. "But say, young man, if you were to take the same trip every night for a hundred years you would never get another experience like that."

"One's enough, thank you," I replied as I tumbled seven feet to the ground and scampered for my Pullman.

The nearby Osage was open most of the year from its mouth, just below Jefferson City, to Linn Creek, a distance of 113 river miles, and to Warsaw, 172 miles, during hte seasonable wet weather of spring and early summer.

"A Ride in the Engine Cab of the Twentieth Century Limited," *The Railway Conductor* 22, no. 3 (March 1905): 168–70.

He Kept His Word

Here is a jim-dandy tale that needs little introduction. Suffice it to say that this 1919 yarn involves a woman, a wrongful hurt, and a great personal sacrifice. And, of course, a train—

"Pardon my curiosity, Billy, but do you mind telling me who that was you just shook hands with—the man with the western look?"

William S. Strong, retired freight conductor, popularly known as "Billy," winked at me as he answered jovially: "Surely I'll take time to tell you, Jack; it's not such a long story."

He pulled out a chair and calmly placed his feet on the edge of my desk, slowly filling his pipe.

"All right, Billy, shoot!" said I. "Local freight's an hour behind schedule, and you can help me pass the time."

"It was like this," he began. "Some ten years ago, when I was still on the job, I had two brakemen, named Jim Frost and Jerry Brown. There's nothing startling about that. I always had two. But the interesting thing about these two was that they were both in love with the same girl.

"Jerry Brown—you knew Jerry, because he was raised handy here—rather had the jump on Jim from the start. Nobody knew where Jim came from and he never told anyone. Just blew in here one day, asked the superintendent for a job, and got it. He was always a quiet, rather bashful sort—lost at a tea party, but hell in a fight! Jerry, as you know, was just the opposite—a regular sport.

"The girl's name was Nellie Van Dyke. She lived up on a farm, not far from the end of the line. Jerry had persuaded Jim, much against his will, to attend a barn dance one night, and that's where they both met her. Jerry, as I said before, seemed to fare better than Jim from the very start, although they were friendly about it, and if one received a little more favor than the other at her hands, there were no hard feelings.

"Whenever we'd pass that farm, they both used to sneak out of the caboose and wave for dear life, in case Nellie happened to appear, and then the flagman would make great sport of them.

"Things went on this way for several months and then one day Jim didn't go out to wave, and I learned that Nellie and Jerry were to be married soon. I pitied Jim Frost. It seemed as if the news had taken all the sunlight out of him, although he never said much, and he and Jerry seemed to be just as good friends as ever, and Jim even served as 'best man' at the wedding. I've an idea he was a pretty gloomy 'best man.'

"Nellie and Jerry settled down here at the junction, and everything was just fine until Jerry got in with bad company, I guess, and took to drinking. Then he began to miss calls and get suspensions, and once he was responsible for a little run-in that smashed up several cars. They gave him three months for that. And all the time Jim was talking to him, and lecturing him, and telling him he ought to do better for Nellie's sake if not his own. And Jerry would tell Jim to mind his own business and let him alone.

"Then one winter night the big crash came. It was dark when we pulled three loads off Hawk Run Colliery siding. It was Jerry's place to throw the switch, but I guess he had been drinking some, for he gave the engineer a signal to go ahead, leaving that facing

point switch open for No. 4, which was due in ten minutes or so. No. 4 crashed into seven empties which were standing on the siding, killing the engineer and injuring several passengers.

"We were still on the siding where we had cleared for No. 4 when we heard the crash.

"'My God,' said Jerry, turning pale, 'I forgot that switch.'

"I ran to the telephone booth, but couldn't get the line for about ten minutes. 'The engineer was killed.' I said, returning. 'They want to know at once who was responsible for that switch.'

"'Great God,' moaned Jerry, 'they'll jail me for that. I'll get ten years at hard labor.'

"Something caused me to turn and look at Jim Frost then. He was white as a sheet, but there was a kind of sneer on his lip, a sort of look of disgust.

"'That's you, Jerry Brown—always thinking of yourself, d—n you! How about that little woman up there—your wife—Nellie?

How will she stand this disgrace you've brought on her by your drinking and your carelessness? It'll kill her, that's what.' He paused to let his words sink in, and Jerry began whimpering like a baby.

"I could see that Jim was struggling with himself, trying to arrive at a decision concerning something, but I was totally unprepared for what was coming next.

"'Jerry Brown, you fool, listen to me. I'm going to give you another chance for her sake—do you get me—for her sake? If it wasn't for her, I wouldn't touch you. As it is, I'll take the blame on myself on one condition, and that is that you'll swear by all that's sacred that you'll never drink another drop of liquor and that you'll do everything in your power to make your wife happy, and to try to become what she thought you were when she married you! There's my offer. Take it or leave it.'

"Jerry grasped at the chance, dog that he was, but at this point I interfered and refused to allow Jim to take the blame.

"'Look here, Billy,' he said, 'you're no friend of mine unless you do. Think of her, Billy. This thing would nearly kill her. And besides, Billy, I can skip right now and they'll never get me. So far as the law is concerned, I'm a wolf in the woods. They couldn't get me there.'

"He kept right on pleading, with the result that I finally gave in. He then made Jerry repeat every word of his offer and swear to it in my presence.

"'Jerry Brown,' he said at parting, 'if you dare break faith with me, I'll come back, no matter how far away I am, I'll come back and I'll take her away with me if I have to kill you first!'

"With that parting shot, Jim grabbed his dinner pail and disappeared into the woods. For a long time I stood and watched the place in the trees where he had disappeared, and Jerry Brown stared sullenly at the ground.

"Jim Frost was, as he had said, a wolf in the woods, for although the sheriffs of three counties scoured the country for him, they secured not a single clue as to his whereabouts. He had disappeared as completely and quickly as though the earth had opened and swallowed him.

"Jerry Brown kept his pledge about a month and then he began to drink worse than ever. This soon resulted in the loss of his job and he became a regular gutter soak. His wife, in hopeless despair, finally left him and returned to her people. You know what happened to him—delirium tremens. That was several years ago.

"You remember when I was visiting the West a few months ago? Well, who do you suppose I ran across out there? Jim Frost, as sure as you live! He's got a big ranch out there and he's doing fine. I told him all about Jerry's death and Nellie's going back to her folks, and of how grieved she appeared to be when I told her of the sacrifice he had made (for Jerry had never told her the truth about it). And he sat right down and wrote her a long letter and she answered it right off, and I reckon they've been corresponding pretty regular lately.

"And that man you shook hands with was—

"You've guessed it—Jim Frost—and he's come back to keep his word."

J. A. Allard, "He Kept His Word," *The Railway Conductor* 36, no. 5 (May 1919): 235-37.

THE GIRL OPERATOR

Theatrical poster from 1899.

In 1881 an Iowa farm girl, Kate Shelley (1865-1912), saved a Chicago & Northwestern passenger train from plummeting through a collapsed bridge. She had clawed her way across the damaged bridge during a storm and got word of the collapse to the next depot down the line. For this she received two medals, $300 in reward money, a gold watch, a half barrel of flour, a half load of coal, and a lifetime pass on the C&NW.

But perhaps more significantly, her act of courage inspired an army of story writers, who would recast the epic event in a hundred different ways with as many different endings.

The barrage of "girl saves train" stories that afterward inundated the market are, for the most part, thickly mired in romantic fluff—so much so that even the Victorian readers probably had a hard time swallowing the tales. One has to wonder if the formula might not have been improved had the would-be heroine faltered along the way and left the onrushing train to its fate!

Still, we have what we have; history does not provide us with an alternative ending. The fact that editors of the day so often printed such stories attests to the popularity of the melodrama and compels us to present a sample here. This one has all the elements of its predecessors, but with more raw-edged realism. It features a female telegraph operator, for women were routinely employed as railroad telegraphers by 1900. The story presumably was written by a woman, though she refuses to give her real name. Whoever was the author, that person knew a thing or two about telegraphy and the job of the night operator. Consider this 1915 adventure the best of the genre—

Third-trick Dispatcher Morrisy was not in love with me. He had made this fact sufficiently manifest during the three weeks which had elapsed since my installment as night operator at Oakton.

He had done what he could to make me regret my rashness in inducing the chief dispatcher to transfer me to the Norwood district.

He had been so successful that I had already committed the indecorum of shaking my fist at the sounder in lieu of his face some fifty-odd times—he being some forty miles distant; while the mere thought of the dispatchers on the district, who had been uniformly kind to me, almost dissolved me in tears.

But my resolution to remain on the Norwood district was unaltered.

Even my first sight of the depot at Oakton, situated a mile from the town, near the banks of a small stream—a location sufficiently appalling to the heart of any night operator, especially to those of the female persuasion—had not shaken my determination, though my heart sank a little.

Second-trick Dispatcher Watts was an old fellow who was good-natured while things were going well and trains running in good shape; but he was the reverse when they were otherwise.

In the main, however, he appeared amiable in contrast with Dispatcher Morrisy. I knew him well, having met him at Currie, from which point he subsequently had been transferred to Norwood.

I was not personally acquainted with Mr. Morrisy, nor did I desire that honor. My wire acquaintance with him was quite sufficient.

Some of the trainmen volunteered the information that he was a good fellow—an opinion which I ironically indorsed. For, although I disliked him, I had not been many nights at Oakton before I knew that he was the most efficient train-handler on that division.

The train sheet was to him a mere chessboard; he moved his men with confidence and played on his nightly game with unerring skill and a swiftness I have never seen equaled.

He could raise heavy blockades in the shortest time on record. When trains were congested around the yard at Woodford Junction, and Dispatcher Watts frantic in his efforts to get them on without delays, I learned to watch for the first stroke of midnight and to listen for the cool "OK, RDM," which announced that Dispatcher R.D. Morrisy had begun his watch. With a feeling of relief I realized that the mental strain of my old friend Watts was over for the night.

Morrisy found plenty of exercise for his skill. The winter season was coming on and regular third-class freights were running in four to eight sections, while quick-dispatch, Nos. 51, 52, and 53, averaged five and six sections each per night, besides the usual complement of passenger trains, specials, and extras.

But, despite the heaviest of the work, Morrisy found time to bully nearly every man along the line.

As Oakton was situated on a two mile stretch of level track, and was a favorable point for the stoppage of freights, it was a heavy train order station, and I came in for my share of the bullying along with the rest. In fact, it soon dawned on me that I received more than my just due. Whether things were wrong or otherwise, the result was the same.

When second No. 81 pulled out of track No. 2, her crew forgetting to close the switch, which was later unnoticed by No. 452, and she ditched her caboose and tore up the switch frog, Morrisy insisted that I must share the blame.

"We need wide-awake operators," he said severely, "who can use judgment, not deadheads! Why didn't you notice the target was set at red and go out and close that switch?"

He threatened to "write me up" to the chief for not answering my call on the telegraph sounder, though I held the record for promptness on the Currie district. Then for several nights he made me go up to the north end of the mile passing track after trains that had been cleared. In a word, I discovered that Dispatcher Morrisy was opposed to the employ of women in the service and was trying to drive me back to the Currie district.

One evening, nearly a month after I had taken charge of the night work at Oakton, I entered the depot feeling somewhat depressed. For several nights preceding business had suddenly slackened and regular trains had moved pretty well on their schedules, rendering my work unusually light.

Time dragged when there was nothing to do, and I stopped at a bookstore, bought a novel, and tucked it in my lunch basket. It was not cold, but there had been rain and the air was chilly. I shivered as I stepped on the platform and looked around at the gloomy prospect; the station was fully a half mile from town. No buildings were near. It seemed isolated.

Some hundred yards south of it, spanned by a long trestle, Current River dragged its shining length. It was a narrow stream and was said to be very deep.

A strange loneliness that was almost fear crept into my soul as I turned away and entered the office. I was met at the door by Mr. Clapp, the agent.

Mr. Clapp was a stout, good-humored fellow; we got on together well, and I had grown to like him.

"Bad time for the owls, Miss Kitty," said he. "We've had a squally day, and the wires are all mixed up. Everything's blocked up in great shape at Woodford Junction, and Watts is half wild."

"Anyone hurt at Beauregard?" I asked, setting my lunch on the desk and divesting myself of my hat and mackintosh.

"Oh, no! No. 89 sidetracked there for the No. 82's, and got some cars off. The main line is all right, but the passing track is tied up for the night. I shouldn't wonder if you had something to do when Morrisy comes on and begins to raise that blockade at Woodford."

"Well, I dread it," I replied, glancing over the train register sheet. "Not the work; but Mr. Morrisy, he's bad enough when everything's going well."

"Oh, RDM's all right when you get to know him!" Mr. Clapp answered. "We used to work together on the L&N. He's crusty, and I don't think he likes ladies on the force. But he don't have any pets."

"If he has I'm not one of 'em—that's certain," I responded, signing the transfer, which read: "Nothing on hand."

"But once a friend, he'd stand by you," pursued Mr. Clapp, buttoning his raincoat. "He lost his job on the L&N through trying to shield one of his operators."

"He's trying to make up for it over here," I retorted. "He is not likely to lose his job shielding any of us. He's shaken my faith in dispatchers. I used to think them pretty nice."

Mr. Clapp laughed as he pulled out a drawer of his desk, exposing a shining revolver. "In case," said he meaningly.

I tapped the pocket of my mackintosh. "I've a gun here," I replied.

"Good for you!" heartily exclaimed my friend, turning to go.

He paused on the threshold and looked back. "I lit the red lanterns, and if you chance to need 'em they're just within the freight room.

"And say, Miss Kitty, keep a sharp lookout after the switch lights. If any of 'em go out be sure to light 'em—especially those at the end of the mile track."

"Yes, I will," I replied, laughing.

Mr. Clapp walked swiftly down the platform and passed out of sight.

I bolted the door, seated myself at the operator's desk in the large bay window, and turned my attention to the wires.

Mr. Clapp was right; they were "mixed." No. 71, the commercial wire, was standing open. I tried the ground—it had no circuit. No. 18, the "through" to New Orleans, was crossed with some foreign wire, and even the dispatcher's, No. 7, was swinging badly.

Dispatcher Watts, battling manfully against difficulties, was keeping the operators on the line off No. 7 wire with the figure "9"—the signal that precedes train orders—and was frantically endeavoring to get trains over the road.

But there were intervals when the wires "went down" altogether and absolute silence reigned. During those intervals I felt lonely and nervous to an unwonted degree. I cared little for the other company when the counters were clicking. I placed some train order pads handy in case of need and, with my revolver on the train register sheet before me, settled myself to read.

At ten-thirty Lineman Edwards, who had been out on the road for hours, found part of the trouble between Cleves and Woodford Junction and straightened No. 7 wire, though he failed to clear the other wires. Immediately after, the dispatcher called me to report whether the third No. 84 had passed.

They were coming. I leaned my face against the window pane and watched them rumble by. The conductor was standing on the rear end of the caboose of third No. 84. He shook his lantern at me. By its light I saw something white flutter from his hand. It was his station report. I reached for my revolver. I never stirred outside without it in my hand. A broad band of light fell from the window across the platform, and I did not think it necessary to take a lantern.

I unbolted the door and stepped out to get the report.

But I was not successful. I stepped back quickly, slammed the door, and turned the key.

I had found myself face to face with a man, standing just below the pale of light.

Typical turn-of-the-century small town depot, Pontiac, Illinois, circa 1902.

Though not really frightened, I felt startled. The isolation of night work had taught me watchfulness, but I had heard no footsteps on the platform.

A minute later I smiled at myself for allowing such a trivial incident to shake me. Still, I know the value of caution in that lonely situation. I examined my revolver and saw that each chamber was loaded before resuming my place at the desk. When I did so I glanced outside. It was dark without, but the light falling over the platform rendered visible objects not illuminated.

The man was gone. This fact did not render me more comfortable.

I was soon absorbed in my book again. An hour later when, after a long silence, the sounder on No. 7 suddenly lifted up its voice in my office call, I positively started.

"ON—ON—WJ." It was Woodford Junction calling Oakton.

"I—ON," I responded.

"Adj fr WO qk," (Adjust for WO quick!) said he.

"WO" was the dispatcher's office at Norwood.

I glanced at the clock. It was half past twelve. Morrisy was on duty. I adjusted quickly, although with difficulty, because of the heavy current.

The first thing I heard plainly was Morrisy's signature, and I promptly broke in.

"Get out!" he snapped angrily, and then he continued: "To BW g a," (Go ahead).

"BW" was Bowes, the division terminal. It seemed I had interrupted a message, for the operator at "BW" "went ahead," and I listened, my hand on the key.

"Flues leaking and may delay us. Delayed ten minutes. Bowes for connection, and picking up Mr. Spencer's private car. No. 10, for Currie. (Sig.) Frazier, No. 4."

I sat up suddenly. I knew no Conductor Frazier on that district.

Surely it was not—but, after all, what was more natural? Conductors were often transferred. I felt my cheeks grow hot. The sounder broke in on my reflections.

"ON—ON—WO—" Morrisy impatiently called me.

"I—I—ON," I answered.

The storm had been gathering some time. I knew it would break soon.

"I want to know why I can't raise that office tonight."

Thus Morrisy, deliberately laying aside abbreviation—something he never did in conversation, save when extremely irritated—addressed me.

"I—" I began, but he cut me short.

"Yes, W. Why dnt u ans?" (Why don't you answer?)

"But the—" It was no use. He broke me again.

"I've bn afr (been after) u 40 mins!" snapped he. "Ts no way to do biz, and I'm tired of it. Nw rpt (report) ure trains, and c if u cant ans up betr, or ull get a letter wi a man in it!"

I obeyed with a mad hand. He was raising the blockade at Woodford for fourth No. 58. One had rolled by and the sixth section was in sight.

It was long past lunch time, and when the sixth No. 81 passed I brought my basket to the desk, feeling unusually hungry.

As I sat down a scratching noise at the window caused me to look up. A man's face was flattened against the pane. It was the face of the man at the door.

The basket fell from my hand. I made a motion toward my revolver and leaned forward.

"What do you want?" I called sharply.

"When is No. 10 due here?"

"At two-thirty," I replied.

"Two-thirty? Nearly an hour yet."

He turned away. A voice in the darkness muttered an indistinct reply.

He was not alone!

I returned to my lunch, but my appetite was gone. I tried to keep a sharp lookout, but the wind had risen and the panes were blurred by a dashing spray of rain. The two men retreated to a sheltered spot on the platform. They evidently had no intent ion of leaving. I could not see them, but I stole into the freight room and located them by their voices.

I tried to resume reading, but could not fix my attention. The unknown men on the platform, the lonely situation, the unusual silence of the wires, all conspired to make me nervous.

I sat still, straining to catch the slightest sound, yet inwardly rebuking myself. A rustling under the desk caused me to start and seize my revolver.

I investigated and discovered a rat. I laughed outright as I replaced my weapon and turned to the train wire. I resolved to shake off the fears that beset me.

Nos. 18 and 71 wires had no circuit, but the sounder on No. 7 was clicking busily.

Woodford Junction was repeating an order from a conductor.

I took up a pen, drew a pad toward me, and copied it idly. It ran: "ORD No. 42 to 1st 51, WJ—OK—VO. No. four (4) eng. 1106 and first (1st) fifty-one (51) eng. 618 will meet at Oakton. (Sig.) Barrett, 1st 51."

"OK—Complete 2:25 a. m.—RDM—WO," responded Morrisy.

"He wants to know wr (where) No. 4 gets it," (the order for the meeting point of the two trains), said the operator.

"At RD if I can ever raise t dam ham."

"Tell him to kick out and not delay t game!" replied Morrisy.

"RD—RD—WO—9!" Morrisy called.

"RD—RD—RD—9—RD—RD—99999999—WO—" he continued.

But RD (Beauregard) did not answer.

No. 10 was already overdue there. Clearly their engine was delaying; they were not making time. It was unusual to make a meeting point between a freight and a fast mail, but Mr. Morrisy was a bold dispatcher. He took chances frequently, and rarely miscalculated.

His motive was manifest. He could get first 51 no farther than Oakton without the possibility of delaying No. 10. He could calculate with no certainty on No. 10's time, as she had lost steadily s ince leaving Bowes, and, as the shortest method, he had made a meeting point between them at Oakton, intending to annul the order to No. 10 at Beauregard, provided she did not reach that point before I reported first No. 51 in the clear at Oakton.

This she was not in the least likely to do unless No. 51 was accidentally delayed.

Failing to raise Beauregard, Morrisy put out the order at Woodford Junction to avoid delaying No. 51, depending on getting it to Beauregard later.

But he had reckoned without his operator. The night man at Beauregard was new to the service. The night was rainy and he had forgotten the importance of keeping the wires adjusted. Morrisy continued calling for thirty minutes or more, interspersing his calls with characteristic epithets:

"RD—RD—dam u! RD—RD—9—je! RD—WO—WO—999—ON—WO."

"I—ON," I responded.

"Watch for first No. 51 cmg (coming) in a let me no. RD—RD—. To ON—WO."

"I," said I.

"First No. 51 in site?"

"Nt et," (not yet).

"Ty shld B cmg. Copy 3." He gave me the order for No. 4. "Let me no wn No. 51 in clear. I want bust tt (that) to No. 4," said he when I had repeated it.

He resumed calling RD snappishly.

After a short interval Beauregard broke in with:

"I—RD—No. 4 by 3:10—RD."

"Whr u bn?" demanded the irate dispatcher.

"Here, but wire had gone dwn," replied RD.

"Yes, a ure gng dwn next! To ON—have ure red lamp redy a flag No. 10 sure if No. 51 dnt get in. No. 10 in site?"

"Aint in site." I replied in the negative.

I had no occasion to use either of the signal lanterns, and found them sitting where Mr. Clapp left them, in the freight room by the coal bin. They burned clearly, their combined light struggling in to effectually dispel the gloom in the long, drafty room.

I shivered when my eyes fell on some coffins among the freight piled in a corner. Picking up the lantern, I turned quite hastily.

Just as I did so I heard footsteps. I paused. I had forgotten the men on the outside. I now heard them seat themselves on the floor against the large freight door, jarring it slightly. Their voices I could hear plainly. What one of them was saying held me as if I was glued to the spot.

"And there's nothing north ahead of No. 10. No. 51 will be the first thing south, and it's tied up somewhere for No. 10. No. 10's engine is leaking—that's what's delaying her. I heard that much before we went to work."

So one of them was an operator. He had been listening at the window.

With what object? Before they went to work—at what?

A chill ran down my spine. I put the lanterns down softly and crept closer to the freight door.

"Are you sure old Spencer's along?" asked a lower voice.

"Haven't I told you I heard a message that his car would be on No. 10's train?" returned the first.

"Didn't both of us hear him tell the roadmaster he's to start for Currie tonight?"

"He'll never get there. That bridge wouldn't hold up a rat. Curse him! He'll never get another chance to kick a man out like he was a dog!"

"We've done the job this time, and it was dead easy with that girl here," was the reply. "I hate to ditch a whole train to get one man, but we'd never catch him any other way. That trestle was unsafe, anyhow. It might have happened any time."

"That's no lie! The wood was rotten in spots," returned the other. "I don't see how it holds together with them timbers sawed through."

"It's likely to go in the river any minute. I never—"

But I waited to hear no more. They were speaking of the trestle over Current River, I knew. I had listened thus far, paralyzed with a horror which beaded my face and hands with cold sweat.

Then one thought leaped from the black chaos like lightning. I alone stood between No. 10 and destruction!

I shook off the numbed spell and stole swiftly back to the office. I went to the window. A glance told me that No. 51 was not in sight. I dared not wait, and turned to the clock. It was three-fifteen—scarcely more than four minutes had passed since I left the room.

Beauregard had reported No. 10 by at three-ten. No. 10's schedule between Beauregard and Oakton covered twenty minutes. There was no time to think. I had just sixteen minutes in which to act.

I extinguished the red lantern with a downward jerk.

Morrisy was calling "ON!" frantically, signing the usual all-compelling "9," but I paid no heed. I took a small rubber match-case from my mackintosh and hid it in my bosom.

Then, the extinguished lantern on my arm and Mr. Clapp's revolver in my hand, leaving my own gun lying on the desk as a blind, I tiptoed to the back window, raised it softly, climbed out, drew down the shade, and in a moment was outside.

The wind was still blowing, but the rain had ceased. I scurried away to the river, making a short cut for fear of detection. The clouds had lifted, and after the first minute I could see objects plainly. I ran my best; I was putting my speed against that of the mighty locomotive, No. 1106, which was pulling No. 10, and I knew that in her failure to make time lay my only hope.

On the next issue of that unequal race hung the life of every human being on the train. But of the many on No. 10 that night one life only was in my mind.

As I neared the river I suddenly checked my speed, wondering how I was to get across.

One of the wreckers had said that the trestle would not hold a rat. Even if it were safe, I should not have dared to cross. They were doubtless on the switch and might see me.

I knew there were no boats nearer than the small landing, a quarter of a mile up the river.

But I stopped scarcely a second. In less than a minute I was running down the bank, my feet sinking in the mud.

Once upon the very brink of the turbid water, I hesitated again and listened. I could hear nothing of No. 51.

My mind was made up. Many months of night duty at lonely way stations had inured me to face situations before which women ordinarily shrink. I let the lantern fall from my arm to my hand, and a new difficulty struck me. Would a bath in the river unfit it for signaling?

There was no remedy; it must be risked. I tore a piece from my underskirt, tied the lantern around my neck, and plunged into the river.

Fortunately, I was a good swimmer, yet I was taking a desperate risk—not for myself, for I had flung all personal fear to the winds; but I thought of the issue of the almost hopeless venture as it concerned that other life rushing toward destruction.

The water seemed liquid ice and the current was strong. The waves had risen with the strong wind and billowed about me in little foamy hillocks. My dress clung in tight folds and impeded the freedom of my legs.

But, although I struggled desperately against these difficulties, despair hung heavily on my heart, and I realized that if I succeeded in reaching the opposite shore alive in all probability it would be too late.

The very agony of haste under which I was laboring nearly defeated my object. I was floundering almost helpless in mid-stream—the water in my eyes and ears—when a long, hoarse, plaintive note sounded.

No. 1106 was whistling for Devil's Gap, a "blind" siding between Oakton and Beauregard.

It struck my ears like an unconscious cry for help and sent the blood tingling to my hands and feet, numbed by the chill water. If I failed, within ten minutes No. 10 would be at the bottom of the river, her passengers and crew—

My strokes grew less furious and more steady. My breath grew labored and I was forced to part my lips. The reaction after the wild run had set in.

But I struggled on. I would save him or my own life would go out in the attempt. For what would life mean to me if I failed?

Within a few moments my feet struck the riverbed. Almost directly I was splashing through water barely waist deep.

With teeth chattering, I stood on shore. There was not a moment to lose. Despite my utmost efforts, the current had carried me some distance downstream. I climbed the soft embankment, dashed through a long wilderness, and finally reached a barbed wire fence which guarded the right-of-way.

I parted the strands of wire as best I could and crept through—the short spikes tearing my skirts.

I scrambled up the steep grade to the right-of-way. I had barely done so when there came a loud, cracking grinding, thundering noise, followed by a jar which seemed to shake the earth. All the water in the river seemed to leave its bed and rise in a column and then rush back with a sudden plunge.

The trestle had collapsed!

I turned and fled down the bank. The wind was gaining strength. The darkness grew more intense.

There was a flash of lightning. The trees skirting the right-of-way sprang into startling relief and were immediately swallowed up in gloom.

Once I fancied I heard footsteps crunching the roadbed and my heart beat rapidly, but it was only the scattering rain drops upon the gravel.

I had not gone many yards when a bright, round disk of light flashed suddenly into view down the track. It was the headlight of No. 10's engine not more than a mile away.

I redoubled my efforts, tearing the lantern from my fastening as I ran. A moment later No. 1106 lifted its deep voice in melancholy cadence at Scott's Crossing.

The headlight grew larger; the rails stretched away and came together in a long, glistening point. I shook the lantern violently to clear it of water, and struggled with the bottom. The spring was stiff and resisted my fingers for a moment, and then gave way.

Fortunately, the match-case was waterproof and the matches were unharmed. One, two, three flared mere blue sparks in the protecting hollow of my hand, sputtered, and died out, refusing to light the wet, greasy wick.

The fourth leaped to the wick. In a trice the blaze was ensconced in the globe, the bottom fitted on, and the lurid danger signal swinging across the track as I ran toward the rushing train.

No. 1106 was vainly trying to save her reputation by making up some of her lost time. The flashing headlight grew larger rapidly;

the steady, pulsing roar deepened in volume. I stopped short in the middle of the track and swung my lantern to and fro.

Engineer Dodds had not seen the signal—that was plain. I raised it above my head to attract his attention.

As I did so a pistol cracked in the distance. The wreckers had seen my red warning.

No. 10 was barely more than a hundred yards distant. I raised the lantern again and shook it frantically. Then, as the train was almost upon me, there came two short notes from No. 1106, and I flung myself from the track—not a moment too soon. With a hoarse scream for brakes the train shot by.

I had a reeling vision of the dimly lighted sleepers as I fell almost headlong into the muddy ditch skirting the embankment of the road. My lantern was put out by the fall. I sat up in the mud, dazed. Then I climbed up onto the track and started after No. 10's lessening markers.

Would they go into the river, after all?

Suddenly the markers became stationary. There was a pause, then a loud, angry snort from the engine, followed by a quick succession of shorter but lighter blasts of the whistle.

The train was backing up. I struggled to my feet. I had been half lying across the end of a cross-tie with my arms upon the rail.

The rear car came to a standstill at a short distance. As I dragged myself toward it a la ntern shone out suddenly from the steps of a middle coach, and it seemed to turn a somersault as its owner leaped down and hurried to the engine. Presently another lantern flashed from that direction. Engineer Dodds was hurrying to the rear.

A voice rang out, loud and clear:

"What's the matter down there, Dodds?"

"The trestle's down!" shouted Dodds.

"What?"

"Trestle's down! The pilot wasn't thirty feet from the bank when I got her stopped. If we hadn't been flagged we'd all been in the bottom of the river now!"

There was not a braver runner on the road than Al Dodds, but his voice was unsteady with excitement.

Lights suddenly twinkled along the whole length of the train. Several windows were raised and frowzy heads looked out. The lights from the baggage coach fell on the grimy Dodds and the trim, uniformed figure of the conductor.

The baggageman squatted in the door and eagerly listened to the excited talk.

"I tell you, boys, we'll never be any nearer passing in our checks than we've been tonight!"

Dodds was saying. "Who could have been up here at this time of night?"

"Must have been the night operator," said Conductor Frazier.

"No, it wasn't," said the baggageman. "For I heard old Watts saying that the night operator here is a woman."

"Well, whoever it was, we must 'a struck him," said Dodds. "I didn't see the light until we were almost on it, and went over in the ditch as we passed."

"Good Lord, Al! We'd better go back and look for him instead of standing here!" exclaimed Frazier. "The fellow may be killed!"

"No, he's not! It's not a fellow—it's I, Frank!" I called out.

I was only a few feet distant now. "And I'm not even hurt," I replied.

"What's the matter now?" demanded an authoritative voice, and a stocky, red-faced man rushed past me and stepped within a ray of light.

I recognized Division Superintendent Spencer, whom I had seen only once.

"What does this—"

He broke off suddenly when he saw me and stared as if petrified.

"The trestle is down! Two men sawed the timbers! I heard them talking about it on the platform just in time to save the train!" I delivered this explanation as well as my chattering teeth would permit.

In the consternation and horror vividly painted on the men's faces I had a sudden revelation of my personal appearance. My dress, torn by the wire fence, clung about me in tight folds. I felt my cheeks tingle, though I shivered with cold.

Mr. Spencer caught up Frazier's lantern and held it up so I was fully revealed.

"What—who is this?" he said. "Why, if it isn't—" cried Dodds, lifting my arm.

"Madam, did you flag this train?" inquired the superintendent.

"I did," I replied.

"But how did you cross the river—in a boat? You—surely didn't swim that river?"

"Yes, I did. And I must get back to the office directly or that dispatcher—"

I dropped the lantern and pressed both hands to my head.

"She mustn't stand here longer—she's dripping wet!" cried Spencer, making a motion as if to strip off his coat.

Mr. Frazier had his about me in a trice.

"I'll take her onto one of the coaches, but I'm afraid none of them are really warmed."

"My stove's red-hot—just lift her up," called the baggageman. In a moment I was shivering in his chair beside the glowing stove.

It was some time before I could give a connected account to the eager superintendent, for my teeth were still chattering.

"You are a brave woman!" he exclaimed when I had finished.

The rest were silent, but my hand was hanging limply over the chair arm, and Mr. Frazier, who was close beside me, managed to press it unseen.

"You're mistaken, Mr. Spencer," I said. "I was badly frightened, but I would not have been human had I stayed in the office."

Mr. Frazier pressed my hand again. A thought struck me and I started up.

"That dispatcher!" I explained. "He was calling me when I left the office. I must get back there and explain. He'll write me up sure!"

"I have sent two men up the river to look for a boat," said the superintendent. "I don't think you need fear the dispatcher. I'll explain matters to him myself. Your conduct of tonight shall not be forgotten."

A few minutes later Brakeman McGuire and the train porter arrived in a skiff which they had found at a landing. Dodds and his fireman, together with two or three armed passengers, were left in charge of the train. The remainder of the crew, with the exception of the flagman, who had been sent to the rear, entered the skiff.

I insisted on accompanying them, despite some remonstrance from the superintendent and Mr. Frazier. They feared trouble with the wreckers. But my nerves were wrought up to such an extent that, strange as it may seem, I feared Dispatcher Morrisy more than any number of wreckers. They finally gave in, and I was bundled into the boat by the impatient superintendent. I noticed that they muffled the lantern to guard against bullets. None of the crew were practiced oarsmen, and some time elapsed before we gained the opposite shore. The light in the depot window gleamed faintly through the rain, and I recommenced shivering, despite the warm rugs in which Mr. Frazier had swathed me.

We reached the station without being molested. There was no trace of the wreckers. Evidently they had decamped as soon as they found their fiendish scheme was balked.

The door was bolted as I left it, and the revolver was lying on the register. Mr. Frazier went around to the window I left unfastened, climbed in, and opened the door. The first sound I heard when on the threshold was: "99—ON—ON—WO—9—"

I ran to the key and responded.

"Wts t matr wi u?" (What's the matter with you?) snapped Morrisy.

"Ntg (nothing) Ive—" I began, but he seized the circuit.

"Yes, uve delayed first No. 52—35 mins, at ED, tts wt uve done! I dnt like to rpt (report) ay 1 (any one), but I'll have to explain tt delay, a Im gng to turn it in as it is. Wy hvnt u givn No. 10s sig to tt (that) 9?"

Before I could reply my hand was snatched from the key by that of the superintendent.

"I'll settle with him," he said. "Frazier, take this girl home and arouse the authorities. Wake up Clapp; he can work the rest of the night."

I thanked Mr. Spencer; I felt sick and dizzy. Mr. Frazier and I left together. As we did so we saw first No. 51 heading into the mile passing track. I learned later that they were delayed by pulling out a couple of drawheads on the grade between Woodford Junction and Cleves.

We walked the whole way in silence, but at the gate Conductor Frazier paused a moment.

"It was all my fault—our quarrel," he said in a choked voice. "I'm not fit to speak to you. Forgive me?"

"Don't think of it any more, Frank; it was your danger that made me brave tonight," I replied.

Two weeks went by before I was able to report for duty. Long before I did so I learned that the wreckers, two power-yard men

From *The Railroad Telegrapher*, **1901.**

who had been discharged by the superintendent, were captured at Norwood and had confessed.

I did not work many more nights at Oakton. Mr. Spencer was as good as his word. Within a month the chief offered me the day work at Woodford—the best position on that district. But I declined the generous offer, and a few days later resigned from the service.

The last night I worked at Oakton, Dispatcher Morrisy said: "Ty tell me ure gng to change ure sig, a leave us for a betr job."

"Do they?" I queried.

"Yes," he wired back, and then continued: "Wl if u hdl (handle) the housekpn keys as well as u do these, ull be all right. It wont seem like t same old smile wn ure gone, but its all in t play aywy!" he said, and it seemed to me that the sounder had taken on a lonesome tone.

"Awakening a Deadhead," The Railway Conductor 32, no. 3 (March 1915): 158-67.

THE TALLOW-POT'S TALE

Fireman with an indispensable tool of his trade, 1918.

Hereafter follows a simple tale. It is the story of a bad day at work; nothing new in that regard. What makes this story so rich and original is the way in which it is told. The year is 1917 and the writer uses every bit of railroad slang then in vogue.

While the meaning of most terms will become apparent as the story proceeds, we will give the reader a little shove at the start, to wit: a tallow-pot is a fireman, a shack is a brakeman, a helper is a second engine, and a hook... well, a hook is pretty much what it sounds like it is—only it doesn't go where our tallow-pot eventually puts it—

W ell, I was refreshed some when I awoke in a bunk at the Y from a good ten-hours' sleep, after that strenuous session on First 303.

I looked at my ticker. It was most eight o'clock. Well, thinks I, they must have overlooked me in the course of events; it's the first time that they've let me get a decent—*Bang! Biff! Bang!* "Got another think, Smoke," says I to myself; "you're discovered."

"Well," says I, "what's the powwow all about? I ain't dead or deaf. Are you after the whole kit of tallow-pots? You'll have 'em all awake with that gentle knock of yours."

"Muffle the chatter and hurry up! They want you for nine o'clock, out of the house," says the caller.

"Where yer been all day?" says I. "Giving a guy a forty-five minute call."

"Oh," says he, "they missed you in the scuffle, somehow. Hurry, now. It's X 2329 for yours." "Did you call Jud?" I asks him.

"Jud who?" he yells.

"Hamilton, the Eagle Eye I came up with," says I.

"Oh, him? He reported sick and went home on Number 10 three hours ago."

As Jud had complained of a bad cold coming up, I wasn't much surprised to find that he'd beat it. Hanging out a cab window on a chilly night when you're rattling through the breeze at a mighty smart clip ain't exactly productive of cold curing results.

I was mighty sorry to lose Jud going back. He's one of those guys a tallow-pot will work mighty hard for to keep the old kettle boiling. He'd a good word for you when you were doing a good job and another when you were trying hard but weren't having much luck—he never forgot that he'd been there once himself.

I'd never had this 2329 I was marked up for, but I knew her reputation—which wasn't anything to brag about. They'd used her mostly for work extras, drawbar specials, et cetera, but, somehow, they'd let her loose on the long end of the Hill Division during a rush spell.

I'd heard of her about a week before, when she'd used up five student tallow-pots and pretty near put the kibosh to a two-year man, who got so peeved when he found she couldn't be kept hot that he started in to wallop the whole blooming crew and ended up by getting a ten-days' vacation—which he needed to get mended up in. This old goat had done all this damage in going ninety-six miles. An' here was me chalked up to stand by the old imp for one hundred and forty miles.

"Huh!" I says. "I see where this trip goes down in history."

Believe me, it did.

Well, as I said before, I had forty-five minutes to dress, eat, and hike three-quarters of a mile to the roundhouse. I was called for nine o'clock, so, as customary, had to be on hand thirty minutes before that to get her ready. After getting on my togs I hustled out to one of those colored-glass lifesaving stations for a feed. It was pretty near half past eight when I got it stowed under my belt and, with something extra tucked under my arm, began legging it down the tracks in the dark.

I had covered most of the distance when I fell over a dwarf switch, cracked my shin, and scraped my elbow. Right then I got a hunch that things were going to be some turbulent that trip, and they started in when I limped into the oil house and asked the old gink with a face like a potlatch bug for my stuff— two lanterns, jug, torch, and a can of signal-oil. He passed over everything but my lanterns.

"A couple of lanterns coming," says I.

"We don't give out lanterns to tallow-pots," says he.

"You don't?" says I. "Well, as how those happen to be mine and I stowed 'em in here, perhaps, it ain't exactly customary for the fire-boy to tote the glims up in this moss-covered, tumbled down, backwoods burg. Just the same, I'm going to take those lanterns along with me," I informs him as I climbs over the counter, takes 'em, and climbs back.

By this time it was close to nine o'clock. I spends another five minutes stumbling around a poorly lighted rubbish-strewn roundhouse looking for the old hog.

When I found her and piled myself and baggage aboard, the Eagle Eye was puttering away at the lubricator. By the light of his torch I saw he was looking as sweet as a tub of new pickles.

"How are yer?" says I.

He responds with a silence that was eloquent.

I lit the gauge-lights and lanterns and was just looking over my equipment, when the Eagle Eye opens up with: "Boy, you'll probably be able to do more if you get a hook and scoop—and don't be all night about it, either, for I'm going to get out of here in about two minutes."

Roundhouse and turntable, Douglas, Arizona, 1909.

"What a nice, sociable old square-head," says I to myself as I climbs down and starts a still hunt. It wasn't any use to look for such things in the oil-house so it was up to me to pinch the stuff from some of the other scrap-heaps present.

After I'd climbed over about eight moguls, whales, hogs, and switchers, and found 'em as empty of such things as the 2329 had been, I began to get more or less peeved. Finally I found a couple of scoops. I always got two—because sometimes the shack got reckless.

They had been good scoops—once; but as I was pressed for time I couldn't be fussy. After taking 'em back and dumping 'em in the gangway, I had to start another voyage of discovery for a hook. I found one—same class as the scoops, which was steerage—a regular old war-horse, about twelve feet long and shaped like a snake doing a dash.

By the time I got back—that is, when I got where the 2329 had been, she had gone. I found her out beyond the coal shed with the shack up taking water. No, he wasn't the same guy that was with us coming up.

When I got aboard, dragging that imitation hunk of crooked iron behind me, I found old pie-face taking a look at what little fire was smoldering. In the light of the fire-door he turned and handed me one of those "I-don't-like-yer-mug" looks.

"Well," says he, "by the looks of that fire anybody would think you were going to heat a little water to shave with."

"Aw, say," says I, "give me a minute to get my wind, and, for the love of Pete, be reasonable. I only got a forty-five-minute call."

"That's what they all say," he comes back at me.

"Who's the conductor?" I asks the shack as we were backing down into the yard.

"Full Tonnage Jones," says he; "know him?"

"Huh," says I, "you bet I know him! Had him coming up on the Cannon Ball."

While they were coupling up and looking over the air I spent the time in getting a fire in that old war-horse. She was a false alarm—that old goat—she'd howl her head off while standing around, but when you got out on the road with her she'd grunt and fuss; but steam? She couldn't heat water for a one-chair barber shop.

The car-grabber climbed aboard, kicking about putting junk like the 2329 on a rawhiding job.

"What are you beefing about?" says I. "All you got to do is repose in the hack and watch my black smoke, while I'm up here shortening my life, putting gray hairs in my head and lumbago in my back trying to make steam enough so old King Solomon over there can waste it."

"How much you got back there, Jones?" asks the shack.

"Twelve hundred ton and a helper over the mountain," chirps Jones, as cheerful as if he was telling us we were going light.

"Whoever christened you, Full Tonnage Jones, sure had the right idea," I says as I ducks down the steps.

Though helper engines usually were assigned to districts with long, steep grades, they could also be found assisting in other situations. Here, a helper is coupled ahead of the assigned engine on a flooded stretch of track in Illinois, 1907. Note the brakemen riding the front end, looking for washouts.

When our helper backed on to us I went up to console with the other slave, and found him to be a young Englishman making his first trip alone.

"My friend," says I, talking to him like a father, "this here is going to be a mighty entertaining and enlightening evening for you."

"Oh, but don't cher know, I like the deuced position," he says.

"Yes, I s'pose so," says I. "What'd you break in on?"

"On a switcher, don't cher know."

"Well," says I, "I do know that before we get this drag over the hump you'll be a darned sightwiser than you are now."

"Oh, I say. How?" says his nibs.

"Never mind," I shouts back at him as I climbs down, "stay by her."

It was just ten o'clock when the brake inspector came along and reported.

We followed Number 218 out of Harrisburg; that is, we started, but we stalled two miles out. As soon as we stopped the Eagle Eye jumped down and took a slant at my fire under the scoop. He didn't offer up any remarks; neither did I, although it kind of irritated me to have him shove me out of the way when I was busy getting her hot again, and not so much as saying, "Pardon me, please."

I knew I had a good fire in her, so he had no chance to howl then.

Say, I'd rather fire a good steamer the whole distance than a poor one five miles. A tallow-pot will work mighty hard to keep a good engine hot. It helps a lot to see that old needle splitting the first cipher of the two-hundred mark; but to take a slant at the vapor clock only to see her tail knocking flies off the one-fifty mark—why, it sort of breaks a fellow's spirit and sidetracks his ambition to work up a "rep" as a crack fire-boy. This was about how matters stood on the 2329. I never had a brighter nor a hotter fire in an engine in my life—but steam?—well, she sure lived up to reputation, all right. We stalled twice more before we reached Waban, the half-way station on the mountain.

While old bitter-root didn't pass out any remarks to me personally, he kept up a running fire of mighty unpleasant remarks to himself and the shack.

Three miles out of Waban we stalled again, and in starting "we got one." In other words, we pulled a drawbar.

"Welcome to our city," I says to the shack as I hits the seat, while he goes back to look things over.

"You couldn't make steam enough to work the whistle on a peanut roaster," the Eagle Eye snaps at me.

"Aw, say," says I, "what can you expect from an old refuse heap like this an' you keeping her way down in the corner? Why, you old leather-head, we've been pulling this outfit, besides pushing that old tub ahead of us. They've got a green tallow-pot killing their fire. I ain't heard their exhaust more'n a third of the time coming up."

With that little bit out of my system, I beat it up ahead to see how they're coming with Johnny Bull. When I climbed up I could see they wa'n't coming at all.

The Eagle Eye was hooking and baling slack, and at the same time he was saying some things that would ordinarily start a fight at a peace conference, but the would-be smoke artist was too near all in to care what was going on just so long as he didn't have to vacate that cushion. He'd quit the game at Waban, and was only waiting to get back to civilization to flit.

"How they coming, Jack?" I asks him.

"Oh—but don't cher know, between this bally, blooming hengine and that profane fellah's cursing, I've 'ad an awful time."

"Guess you found it some enlightening, after all, didn't you?" I asks him with a smile.

Well, I got back and kicked down lumps and dust till she had a full pit, then I hits the seat. It took just an hour to get back and set off the boxcar that had lost the drawbar, pick up the drag again, and get going. Half a mile to the lee of the summit the injector began breaking, and we had to beat it for water.

Say, we were having a lovely time.

When we got back to the drag, picked it up, and finally got over the hump we had been on duty seven hours, six of which had been spent getting over the mountain. We got a red order board at Houser; the shack hikes it in after the orders, the helper cut off, backed across, and beat it.

"Hey!" the shack hollers at the Eagle Eye. "They want to know where you've been all night."

When he came out he was just as quiet and peaceful as a Kansas cyclone, and then some. In the meantime I'd been busy. I'd put the blower on wide and got both injectors working, having made up my mind to get her old boiler full just once.

I got her full, all right, for when the Eagle Eye opened the throttle he got a dunking, which didn't help to make him any more sociable.

"Say," he splutters, "I'll turn you in at Eastfield."

"Go as far as you like," I informs him. "But let me tell you right here I'll not let any grouch- generating throttle-puller make me quit, if we stall every ten feet!"

This flow of hot air didn't help matters any. He had it on me, anyway you look at it; and, just to let me know, he put his foot against the Johnson-bar, slammed it down into the corner, and kept it there pretty near all the way.

Say, that old hog had me backed against the ropes, groggy and stalling for wind before we reached the "Big Hole." My fire was clinkered, the flues leaking, and the flue-sheet honeycombed. The shack was on the tender half the time, shoveling over diamonds and occasionally giving the hook a dunking in the tank to cool it off. Then he'd jump down and give me a lift. That shack was a prince; a nicer guy never rode the head end.

When we stopped for the motor at the Hole I was ready for the count. Some folks wouldn't have thought as much of a suite at a swell hotel as I did of a chance to ride that old seat for fifteen minutes.

From the east end of the Hole to Eastfield was mostly easy going, but with that old ruin of human architecture on the right side it was just the opposite. I'd rather have fired fifty miles uphill for Hamilton than five down for that guy. I guess he had an idea that the old scrap heap would turn up her toes if he didn't keep that injector humming—unless he enjoyed hearing it sing.

If we were standing, would he fill her up? Well, not so you could notice it. He'd just let her howl till we were ready to start, then he'd give it to her. I don't know whether it was bum judgment, or just a sixty horse-power, six cylinder grouch, that made him act so cussed.

And that with the way I had worked to get steam enough to keep the outfit moving! I had to hook her with the injector working—raking the fire quick—so as to lose as little steam as possible during the process. It was wearing me out, and when we pulled into Eastfield, after fourteen hours of mighty strenuous exercise, I was a tired smoke artist.

"Well," says the shack, "I guess they'll tie us up here for rest."

"Believe me," says I, "I sure am in favor of it."

Before the car-grabber and head man came out of the telegraph office with our instructions I was on the seat, dead to the world. It didn't last long, though. I sat up and took notice when the conductor yelled in my ear: "Two hours more, boy. We're going to have 'em shake the fire down a bit, take coal, and wheel 'em again!"

In the meantime old funny-face had asked for a new fire-boy, so the engine dispatcher informs me.

"For the love of Pete, get him one," says I.

"Boy," says he, "I know how it is. That combination you're up against would surely corrupt you, so do the best you can and stay with it."

"Well," says I, climbing aboard the old hog again, "I'm back for a third term."

The hostlers had nearly killed my fire, leaving a lot of green coal on the grates—a good foundation for a bunch of clinkers—and when I started to build it up I discovered that someone had got away with my hook. I immediately climbs up and sits down, informing the Eagle Eye that when they bring it back I'll get busy, and not before. After considerable fluent argument, he climbs off and beats it for the hostler's shanty, and immediately a hostler appears about five feet ahead of the old boy, who's making violent passes at the hostler's tail-lights.

"Fat chance," says I to the shack, as we were pulling out, "of our getting anywhere with a green fire in this old goat, with the load we're dragging."

For a tired tallow-pot I kept after her pretty hard. I was just going at it mechanical like and making frequent trips to the water-jug. After shaking, hooking, sweating, grumbling, and juggling the black diamonds for fourteen and a half hours, it's apt to put kinks in your joints. And with the coal-dust irritating every pore and clogging your breathing apparatus, with your hands blistered from a red-hot hook—why, it's mighty hard to do much enthusing about a tallow-pot's job.

You chaps who wish you were a fireman when you see one riding through the station, leaning out the cab window, smiling at the female population as if it was all he had to do, ought to take a ride with that guy over one of those hundred-and-forty-mile pikes and watch how he earns his coffee. A lot of you fellows would like it as much as the student tallow-pot I had one night. He rode the cushion forty miles, watching me bale coal, then he climbed down and opined that his back was getting sore, so he guessed he'd go back to the caboose and lie down. When we got in he showed up long enough to say "s'-long" and reckon he'd go back to that job on the 'lectrics.

At Rocky Hill we got a message from the dispatcher, saying that our time had been extended four hours on account of "engine being

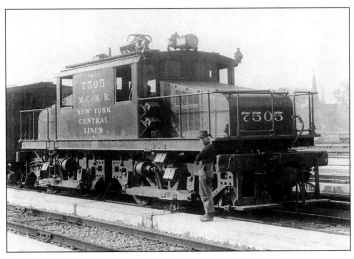

An electric locomotive, Detroit, 1910. Electric locomotives received their power from an overhead line and were used where smoke from conventional engines created a problem. This "steeple cab" electric was used to pull trains through the Detroit River tunnel.

on pit at Eastfield." And we'd been on the pit just thirty-five minutes. Right then I informed the con and Eagle Eye that the minute my sixteen ho urs and thirty-five minutes were up I was done.

"You corporation slaves can stay with this shebang till the cows come home," says I. "But I retire for eats and sleep at Valley Falls, if we make it. If we don't—well, take it from me, I quit on time."

When we pulled up at Valley Falls I had ten minutes to spare.

"Well, bo," says I to the Eagle Eye, pulling my ticker, "ten minutes an' I'm done."

"We'll see about that," says he, beating it for the telegraph office.

I trails him to see that he don't slip anything over on me.

"Tell J.D.," says he, "that fireman on X 2329 quits the engine, refusing extension of time."

The reply was: "Tell that fireman to either obey our instructions or resign."

Then I blows. "You tell J.D., for me," says I, "that I'll neither accept his phony time extension nor resign. And that goes both ways."

I'd done a trick for the Western Union once, and could pound the brass a bit myself, so when the sounder snapped out, "Tell that tallow-pot to obey instructions and shut up," I opens the key and fired back, "U GTH with my regards," signs my name, closes the key, and beats it for the engine with blood in my eye.

I climbs aboard, grabs the hook, puts a kink in it, and shoves it into the firebox. Then I bale coal into her till she's black half way to the crown sheet, shoots in the scoops, bangs the door, grabs up my stuff and hikes back to the telegraph, where I'm being discussed some fluent; but what they'd had to say if they had known what I'd done to the old hog is left to the imagination.

I pushes the operator out of my way and connects with the key again, calling "Ds," the dispatcher, and signing "VF," the call at Valley Falls.

"Don't butt in here," I informs the operator, who's getting nervous having me monkeying with his instrument. "I'm a member of the Hill Gang—sure death when riled—and I'm all stirred up right now."

"I, I, DS," clicks the sounder.

"Hr msg," I send, "(To) JD, Supt. Mutiny on X2329. Been boiling water in this old junk pile seventeen hours. I need rest; a feed and the hay for mine. The old hog needs undertaker. She died with a full stomach. (Sig) The Tallow-Pot."

"There," say I, "I'm done."

Charles W. Tyler, "The Mutiny on X-2329," *Brotherhood of Locomotive Firemen and Enginemen's Magazine* 62, no.2 (January 15, 1917): 12-14.

An Obstinate Farmer

Trains were meant to run on time. Whether or not the reader accepts this as truth is a matter of choice, probably based on personal experience. But certain trains definitely were supposed to run on time. Trains carrying a name such as "The Fast Mail" were required by contract with the Post Office Department to run on time, or else forfeit their earnings.

*Yet even a fast mail train could encounter a detriment to its schedule; it might even be in the person of **An Obstinate Farmer.***

Chicago, Dec. 26 [1890].—The Rock Island express train due in Chicago at 10:50 o'clock this morning was an hour late. The engineer had a dispute with a farmer about the right of way, and an hour passed before the argument was finished. There was some strategy used by the trainmen, for they chased the farmer into the city, and then had him arrested for obstructing the railroad.

Farmer John Reardon left Will County this morning and started to drive to Chicago. He had a good horse and a spring wagon. At Washington Heights he stopped to get a drink and inquire the shortest way to the center of the city. He was told that the shortest route was along the Rock Island track. Farmer Reardon took the hint and started his horse up the track. He was only a few minutes ahead of the express train. A long ribbon of curling smoke marked the course of the fast mail, and Farmer Reardon glanced behind him to see how far the express train was away. A moment later the locomotive leaped into view. The engineer sighted Farmer Reardon and set the air brake, and the same time pulling open the whistle valve in a series of wild shrieks. The farmer only laughed and made up faces at the engineer. He would not move from the track.

The train hands held a consultation and decided that Farmer Reardon was a bad man, and probably had a gun. The locomotive was run up until its nose touched the rear wheels of the farmer's wagon, and the slow procession moved on toward South Englewood. At this point a dispatch was sent to Captain Horace Elliot, who, with a detachment of police, hurried to the rescue of the fast express.

Farmer Reardon, with his spring wagon, half full of shelled corn, was taken to the Englewood police station. He says he had the right of way, and intended to leave the track when he came to a good road.

"An Obstinate Farmer," *The New York Times*, December 27, 1890.

High Speed Johnnie

Call them trolleys, street railways, or traction, they were the city bus lines of their day, and their day lasted well into the twentieth century. It was the trolley that made it possible for the average worker to live more than a short walk from his or her place of employment. And a trolley could take a family to an amusement park, to a shopping district, or simply provide a cool, breezy ride on a hot summer evening.

*The only drawback to a trolley was that it often ran slowly. It had to; after all, passengers got on and off at nearly every corner and the tracks conformed to every hill and valley and frequently bent into right-angle turns. No, indeed, a trolley line was not a race course—unless the motorman got in a hurry, as did **High Speed Johnnie.***

Several years ago, a hard-hearted trainmaster fired me off the Alton, and after roaming over the country without landing a job, I wound up at Omaha.

I searched the town over for work without success, when I learned that the street railway company wanted a few motormen. Through the help of a friend of the superintendent, I was sent out to learn the road and the method of operating the cars.

I served my ten days' student service without mishap, and then caught a Dodge street car, one cold sleety morning, as my first trip. I had no trips out of the ordinary until about eight o'clock, when I was going south on a crowded car. As we had our quota, the conductor told me to highball all the streets unless he rang me to stop to let off passengers.

As I started down the hill from the high school, I found that I could not control the car on the slippery rails. Being new at the business, I got rattled, and we coasted rapidly down the hill. I rang the bell as if I was a fire engine running to a fire, and teams and pedestrians rushed out of my way. One fool girl came out and flagged me as I approached Sixteenth Street. I kept the gong ringing, but she stood in the middle of the track, a trick some of the people used when they wanted to stop a car that was overloaded.

I thought sure that I was going to run over the girl, but I leaned out and yelled at her that I was running away, and that I would run over her if she did not get out of the way.

When that damsel discovered that I could not stop, there came a frightened look over her face, and, with a yell, she turned a flip-flop over backwards just as I rushed past.

I'll bet she never stood in front of another car!

Of course, the "fairy" turned me in, and I received a stiff calling down from the "old man." He certainly raked me over the coals!

I then caught one of the big cars on the Omaha and Council Bluffs line for my next day's work. It did not take me long to discover that the cars were equipped with high-speed motors and were able to make over thirty miles an hour.

At the junction tracks at the car barns on Avenue A, we had instructions to reduce to four miles an hour. On the second trip to Council Bluffs, I had the car "up in the air" as I approached the car barns. Thinking that the superintendent was in Omaha, I decided to take a chance of running the crossing at full speed.

I had a beautiful "swing" on the car and we hit the crossings about twenty-five miles per hour. As I looked back with a grin on my face, that said grin quickly faded when I saw the superintendent glaring at me from one side of the car barn.

I knew I was in for trouble, and so I was not surprised when I came back on the Omaha trip to find a motorman at the crossing to relieve me. The "old man" was there, too, and what he said to me was plenty! "You are too much of a 'High-speed-Johnnie' to suit me!" he said, "and I ought to fire you, but I will give you another chance. You are suspended for ten days, and I hope that when you come back you will have sense enough to obey the rules and will do as I want you to!"

I loafed about for ten days, killing time as best I could. It was then bitter cold and I was glad when my time was up and I was told to report for work again.

On the second trip that I made the morning I went out, I made a trip up to Fairmont Park in Council Bluffs. I had an easy riding car, and what seemed to be a fine brake. So on the trip down the hill, I let off the brake, and let the car run rapidly on upper Broadway. As I approached the curve on the junction to Pearl Street and Avenue A, I started to set up the brake. To my horror, it did not work promptly, and with a lot of jolting, the car jumped the track on the curve, and

From *Century Magazine*, 1906.

ran across the pavement. Of all the yelling and screaming that the passengers did, I never heard the like before nor after!

The car crashed into a telephone pole before it came to a stop. But the force of the collision broke the pole, and it fell into the front of a dry goods store, smashing the plate glass show windows. Believe me, there was some excitement around that particular corner of Council Bluffs! I thought for awhile that they were going to mob me, and I was glad of the arrival of a couple policemen, who soon quieted the crowd.

The "old man" was raving when he reached the scene, and he could only stutter when he saw me for a moment. Then he opened up on me, bawled me out until I cussed him back, and fired me bodily.

I have not attempted to get a job on a street railway since that time, but have stayed on the railroad where a man who is a "High speed Johnnie" can get out and speed up a little without getting fired, and where the faster a man runs, if nothing happens, the better he is liked!

W.H. Henry, "High Speed Johnnie," *The Railway Conductor* 33, no. 1 (January 1916): 10-12.

ASLEEP ON DUTY

Anyone who has worked the night shift knows how wonderfully delicious it would be to fall asleep on duty. We humans are not meant to stay awake all night. Motivated by a biological clock embedded in us all, many the night worker has made an "arrangement" to get in a few winks while on the job. There's always the risk, of course, of being caught. And that usually means getting fired, or, in the case of the railroad telegrapher, the penalty could be much worse. One will therefore forgive the teller of the following true tale from the 1890s for choosing to remain anonymous—

Telegraph operators are usually reminiscent fellows, and the veterans among them delight in telling their experiences. Of course some of their stories may be a trifle exaggerated, but they generally possess at least one unique feature—they are based on something that happened over a stretch of wire perhaps 100 or 200 miles in length.

Occasionally one reads of an extraordinary adventure of an operator at a small and lonely railway station out West, or of perilous experiences in war times, and the impression has become quite common that telegraphers stationed on this side of the Rocky Mountains seldom have other than the most commonplace, routine existence with nothing in it of more than passing interest. As regards the operators for railroad companies, that supposition is wrong.

Within twelve hours' ride of this city there are scores of railroad telegraph offices where an operator is employed day and night to look after both the telegraph and the station.

On many of the roads in New England the night stations are a dozen or fifteen miles apart, and some of them are a quarter or a half a mile from the nearest dwelling house. At these places a night operator is on duty from 7 in the evening till 7 in the morning. A reporter chanced to meet recently a veteran "key twister" who was for several years in the employ of a railroad running through Maine and New Hampshire and up to the White Mountains. This operator sometimes found himself in a pretty tight box, and his account of one experience illustrates the close shaves that railroad telegraphers have now and then.

"Station H, where I worked," he said, "is a night station on a single track railroad in New Hampshire. G, the nearest night telegraph station north of it, was eight miles away, and N the nearest one south, was twelve. My duty in summer was solely that of operator; in winter I also looked after the fires in the waiting rooms.

"There was seldom much operating to do at night, and it was always easy to keep awake until 1 o'clock, when I usually ate lunch. Even at that hour the time didn't pass very slowly in summer, but on cold and stormy nights in winter, when I had to stay constantly indoors, the greatest effort was needed to keep from falling to sleep.

"After 9 o'clock all the trains that passed were freights, and there were half a dozen southbound and as many more northbound in the course of the night. It was part of my duty to note the time that each of the trains passed my station and report it at once to headquarters at A—the same rule applying to all the operators on the line. That was one of the customs which made it danger ous for an operator to fall asleep, if only for five minutes. Another thing that annoyed him and often made him swear was the roll call. This consisted of

From *Cosmopolitan*, 1921.

the train dispatcher at A office (fifty miles south of H) calling each office on the line every half hour, beginning with the one nearest his own. The station that failed to answer a roll call had a black mark placed against it at A, with a record of the time when the call was given. At first the roll call made all the boys look sharp and toe the line, but they soon found a way to cheat it.

"The main wire running through H was considerably more than a hundred miles long; and on a wire of that length it is quite impossible for an operator at its terminus to tell by the sound which of two or more offices not more than twenty-five miles apart is doing the telegraphing, unless the sending operator signs his station call. Knowing this, several of the 'owls' on the line arranged to take turns with each other in answering the roll. For example, the operator at G would answer my calls between the hours of 1 and 3, and I would attend to his from 3 to 5. What a cracking good way this was to baffle the train dispatcher, we thought, and the exchange of duty between us was kept up for a long time; in fact, almost too long, so far as my own case was concerned. I refer to an incident that took place during the winter of 1885, which for a few hours nearly froze the marrow in my bones. It happened like this:

"Through freight No. 241, northbound, was due at my station at 1:35, and was scheduled to meet southbound freight No. 284 at P, fifteen miles farther up the road. No. 241 was scarcely ever behind time, and the two trains usually met at P without requiring telegraphic orders. The night in question was very cold and stormy; fully three feet of snow had fallen and it was still coming down very fast, while a high wind was piling it in big drifts across the track. On a night like that, the incessant humming of the wires outside the station is enough, of itself, to put a sentinel to sleep and that, coupled with the hour, 1:15, and an office temperature of 80 degrees, was more than my weary frame could resist. I fell asleep, knowing, of course, that G would, according to our arrangement, look after my roll calls. After what seemed to me about like twenty minutes, but what was really more than two hours, I was awakened by the sharp clicking of the telegraph instrument near my head.

"'Qk 12' was being made with great rapidity, the call for my office preceding it. I knew it was the train dispatcher, the abbreviation meaning 'Quick! We want you to hold a train.'

"I answered the call, and the command came back quickly and sharp: 'Hold No. 241 for orders.'

"'OK,' said I, and immediately hung the proper signal, a red lantern, outside the door.

"Then I came to my senses and looked at my watch.

"Twenty-five minutes past 3! And I had heard no train in almost three hours. Had No. 241 got past, I wondered? I found that it had left N at 12:40, and the run from N to H usually took about fifty minutes. I knew the storm would probably delay the train somewhat, but two whole hours? It wasn't likely. Then I heard No. 284 reported from P, and knew she had received orders to meet No. 241 somewhere between P and H.

"What if No. 241 had got by me and was trying to reach P for the down freight! In that case the two trains were bound to crash together in the storm; there was no help for it. My excitement was increased by the repeated calls of the train dispatcher to ask if No. 241 was in sight.

"'Not yet,' I answered, trembling lest my hopes were in vain.

"Three thirty-five and no train. I went out on the platform and listened. Not a sound could be heard above that of the wind, and an engine's headlight wouldn't have been visible ten rods away.

"I went back, 'grounded' one of the wires, so as to cut out A office, and called G, hoping to find out whether No. 241 had reached there. No answer. Then I remembered that from 3 to 5 was G's time to 'bunk off,' and knew it was useless trying to get him.

"Ten minutes more, and the freight had not arrived.

"'Sure it hasn't gone?' asked the train dispatcher excitedly as though doubting me.

"'Sure,' said I.

"'For God's sake, don't let it get by you!' he urged.

"Well, 4 o'clock came, and my courage was giving way. I could see how two hours or so might be needed for a freight to go twelve miles on such a night, but three hours and over! So slow a run had never been known on the road.

"What was to be done? To admit my uncertainty meant the loss of my job, and to brave it out any longer seemed almost criminal. In my despair I finally decided to tell the train dispatcher the plain truth—that I had been asleep at my post, and that No. 241 probably went by more than an hour ago. The fact would be known in a few hours anyway, I argued, and I would then be arrested for causing death, convicted of criminal negligence, and sent to prison.

"It was then 4:15. I drew a long breath and went over to the telegraph desk. Headquarters was again calling to ask if the train had arrived, and I broke in abruptly:

"'You may as well know that—' but the sentence was never finished. I heard a faint puffing and grating, and looking out saw the engine of the belated train opposite my office window. My heart leaped up about a foot, and taking a firm grasp on the key of my instrument, I announced:

"'No. 241 h-e-r-e!'

"Deep snow, a terrific wind, and the blowing out of a cylinder head on the engine had caused the delay.

"Maybe all's well that ends well, but that experience put an end, then and there, to my practice of sleeping while on duty."

"A Telegrapher's Story," *The Railroad Telegrapher* 14, no. 6 (June 1897): 475-76.

NIGHT OF THE WOLVES

Angus Sinclair, from *Development of the Locomotive Engine*, 1907.

Comes now a tale of raw adventure. The author, Angus Sinclair, Ph.D (1842-1919), began his railroad career in Scotland. He came to the United States in 1873 and devoted himself to railroad publishing and engineering. His numerous writings were found in the leading railroad trade magazines of the day, and he was the author of a definitive history of the steam locomotive.

The following true story is somewhat of a departure for Dr. Sinclair, for it has little to do with machinery. It is, rather, an account of human bravery—

There are deeds of heroism performed every day in a matter-of-course fashion by our railroad men that would entitle them to honorable decorations were their actions done in spheres where gallantry and daring and endurance were rewarded. In the battlefield of industry, bravery and conspicuous courage are supposed to earn no special reward. They are the matter-of-course attributes of many occupations. Hundreds of heroes who have displayed these attributes in the saving of human life or in the performance of daily duties go in the course of nature to their graves without knowing that they have performed deeds worthy to be commemorated beside the acts of glory which have made other names immortal.

Such thoughts passed through my mind one evening in a quiet house in Kansas as I listened to H. R. Nickerson, formerly general superintendent of the Santa Fe, tell, for the amusement of his guests, some reminiscences of railroading on the frontier of civilization. In relating his personal performances Mr. Nickerson was like Bill Smedley's frog after its phenomenal leaps, perfectly modest and unconscious of having done anything out of the common.

We had been talking about the hardships endured by trainmen in fighting snow.

"We have not been much troubled with snow on the Santa Fe of late years," remarked Mr. Nickerson, "but in the early days of the road's history we got enough to last us to the end of the chapter. When we first stretched out toward the mountains, the prairies and plains were perfectly bare, and the snow was swept for miles to the nearest lee spot. Away about '76 I was conductor of a passenger train and we got stuck in the snow about twenty miles west of Dodge City. We toiled and struggled to get out of a cut where we were stalled, but a fierce blizzard was raging and the snow drifting over the plains unchecked by bush or brake filled up the cut quicker than we could work it out. We had been out for a day and night and the situation was getting serious. The train was full of passengers, many women and children among them, and there was not a morsel of food to eat. Dodge City, over twenty miles away, was the nearest habitation.

"Being a telegraph operator, I carried an instrument with me. Thinking that a relief party might be sent out, I climbed a telegraph post and made connection with the wire, intending to ask Dodge City to send provisions. I called and called, but no Dodge City or other haunt of civilization could be raised. The wires were down, but I did not know that then, and wasted much valuable time trying to establish communication that was hopelessly cut off.

"When at last I realized that the calling for help over that wire was useless, and that there was no hope of the storm soon abating, I made up my mind to walk to Dodge City. The other trainmen and even the passengers declared it was too risky, but I could not sit still for another night and look at those women and children crying with hunger.

"I wrapped myself up well, tied some bagging over my shoes and started out on the twenty-two- mile tramp. The cold wind was blowing with cutting force and the snow kept falling, falling as if the upper air were a reservoir with a never-ending supply. It did not fall fast, but kept up a steady downpour as if it had set out to keep up the operation for a month.

"There is a peculiarity about the kinds of snowfall. If it comes down in great flakes that nearly monopolize space in the air, the snow is likely soon to turn to rain. If a finer snow falls in blinding density it soon exhausts the supply and stops. But when it keeps falling steadily, gently, as if trying to husband its strength, you may depend on having a liberal supply for days.

"This was the kind of snow which I had to encounter. It kept falling with painful monotony, but it never rested. Before reaching the ground it joined a moving tide of snow that was wafted before the wind in search of a resting place. The vast plains seemed to be a sea of moving snow. Silently and quietly it moved along in its white purity, too light evidently to harm the twittering birds, but woe to man or beast that sought shelter in a spot where protection from the wind permitted the snow to rest.

"With the thought only of my passengers in my mind and Dodge City for a magnet at the end of my vision, I kept trudging onward. The telegraph poles were the finger-posts that pointed to safety. Sometimes I walked on the track and sometimes on the prairie, but I never failed to keep within sight of the telegraph poles. When the snow or drift was so thick that I could not see from one pole to another, I counted the seconds, and if the next pole did not appear at the right time I turned toward the track and by that regained my bearing. The wind kept steadily on my left, so that it helped as a guide, for the track was straight.

"The tramp was toilsome. Now I would be walking through soft snow that broke through at every step; then I would suddenly stumble into a covered slough or buffalo wallow and be half smothered before I could again reach firm footing. A great part of the way the track was raised slightly above the plain and the wind kept it fairly clear of snow, so that the walking was good. At other places there were small cuttings which were drifted level, and these parts sent me away from the track.

"The mileage numbers on the telegraph poles told me that Dodge City was yet far away when the shadow of a lurid gleam in the west intimated that the sun was going down. Toward nightfall certain forms had flitted past within my line of vision that gave me some uneasiness. They were prairie wolves—cowardly, harmless animals as a general thing, but I did not know how they might act in the case of a lonely tramp, encountered when they were stimulated to courage and fierceness by hunger.

"I carried my signal lamp, and thinking that it might be some obstacle to any of the wolves that might be inclined to eat my hams for supper, I proceeded to light it. That was no easy job. The oil was frozen and the lamp would not burn. As dusk was falling I began to feel certain that the lighted lamp was a beacon that would frighten my enemies and I determined to make it burn. To accomplish this I groped under the snow for some bunches of dry grass, got down with them in a sheltered spot and started a small fire. On this I held the fountain of the lamp long enough to melt the oil, then lighted it without difficulty.

"When I started up to go after lighting the lamp several wolves were snarling within sight. As the shades of night waxed deeper the animals became bolder and more numerous. They kept pressing toward me, yelling and snarling at each other and then staring at their intended victim with blazing eyes, but a wave of the lamp would send them scampering away.

"At first they would run far enough for most of them to be out of sight, but they gradually grew bolder. They kept pressing closer upon me and I continued to swing the lamp at them without making much impression. I was beginning to imagine how the first bite of their teeth would feel and how long it would take them to eat me up. I had no intention of permitting this performance to go on without resistance, and I had my revolver ready for the emergency which seemed impending. I noticed that one gaunt-looking fellow was more enterprising than his companions. He went the shortest distance at the swing of the lantern and returned first to the charge.

After making half-hearted attempts he made a spring at my leg and received a bullet from my revolver.

"There was a great hurrying to the front and rear and I kept moving ahead while the wolves lingered to pick the bones of their comrade. The feast did not satisfy their longings for the good things of this life, for I had not passed many telegraph poles when the pack was within sight again.

"But they appeared to reason that there was some dangerous relation between the swinging of the lantern and the shot that gave one of their number as supper for his friends. They had no taste for figuring as the principal at that kind of a feast. For a time they kept without reach of an easy shot, but their memory of the disaster that happened to their gaunt member was short lived, or the necessities of their appetite were pressing. By degrees they crowded closer around me. A swing of the lantern would frighten them beyond bounds at first, but gradually its terrors waned.

"I kept plodding forward, doing my very best to keep the hungry brutes at bay, but watching an easy opportunity for another victim. I had not to wait very long. The first of the pack to display conspicuous enterprise received my next shot and he was near enough to get it straight. The hosts scattered again, and again they united to pay the last tribute of affection for their relative. Their funeral ceremonies were not protracted. I had not time to grow lonely in my solitary journey when they were beside me again singing their eerie requiem, which I feared would soon apply to myself. Between rubbing my ears, swinging my lantern and keeping a watchful eye on my escort, I was kept busy. The drama that became a tragedy to two of the wolves was enacted twice again, but no sign of the hospitable dwellings of Dodge City greeted my longing eyes.

"The cold and the fatigue and the hunger (for I had not eaten anything since the previous day) must have begun to affect my

From *Frank Leslie's Illustrated Newspaper*, 1872.

senses, for during the last part of the journey it appeared to me that a wave of wolves was moving over the country as the waves of snow had been seen moving in daylight, but I continued to swing my lantern and hold out my revolver. The impression came that the whole thing was immensely funny, and I must have laughed loudly at the absurdity of the scene. This was the feeling pervading me when I stumbled into Tom Dowd's saloon at two o'clock in the morning.

"This was the only house in the town that had a light burning, and there I went, followed to the door by the wolves.

"I remember vaguely a crowd of men getting around me and of their dragging me outside and beginning to rub my face and ears with snow. I was rather badly frozen, but soon was myself sufficiently to explain what was wanted. A relief party was organized within an hour. A large sleigh was loaded with provisions, and before daylight broke we were far on our way to the spot where many hungry people were waiting to be fed."

Angus Sinclair, "A Heroic Conductor," *The Railway Conductor* 25, no. 3 (March 1908): 176-78.

A NOVEL BATTLE

Cy Warman, from *Weiga of Temagami*, 1908.

In a branch of literature that attracted many competent entrants, Cy Warman (1855-1914) was widely regarded as the dean of railroad story writers. At different times in his life Warman was a railroad engineer, a journalist, a short story writer, and a poet. One of his poems, written about his wife, was adapted to music in 1893 and became a hit song entitled, "Sweet Marie."

This next offering, penned while Warman was living in Paris, takes us high into the Colorado Rockies to witness a contest between two machines designed to remove heavy snow from the tracks. That experience then brings Warman to recall his own days as an engineer working out of Salida, Colorado, when the only way to get through the snow was to punch into it

with a plow and hope for the best. Make no mistake about it:
bucking the snow on a mountain railroad was no easy ride—

Snow bucking with a pilot plow is dangerous business. However, there is very little of it to do in these days. Now a road that is able to accumulate a snowdrift is able to own a rotary plow or snow excavator. These machines are as large as a coach and as heavy as a locomotive. The front end is funnel- shaped; and instead of throwing the snow away it swallows it, and then spurts it out in a great stream like water from a hose at a fire.

Inside the house, or car, there is a boiler as large as a locomotive boiler, with two big cylinders to furnish power to revolve a wheel in the funnel-shaped front end. This wheel is like the wheel of a windmill, except that the fans or blades are made of steel and are quite sharp. As the plow is driven through the drifted snow by a locomotive—sometimes by two or three of them—the rapidly revolving wheel slices the snow from the hard bank and draws it into the steel chest, where the same rotary motion drives it out through a sheet-iron spout.

Once at Alpine Pass, on a summer branch of the Union Pacific, I saw one of these machines working in six feet of snow that had been there six months, and was so hard that men walked over it without snowshoes. It was about the middle of May; the weather was almost warm at midday, but freezing at night. A number of railroad and newspaper men had gone up there, eleven thousand feet above the sea, to witness a battle between two rival excavators. The trial was an exciting one, and lasted three days. Master Mechanic Egan, whose guest I was, was director-general, and a very impartial director, I thought. The two machines were very similar in appearance; but instead of a wheel with knives, one had a great auger in front, the

A plume of white and the exhaust of smoke and steam marks the progress of a rotary plow as it eats into a snow slide, circa 1910.

purpose of which was to bore into the snow-drift and draw the snow into the machine, as the chips are drawn from an auger hole by the revolving of the screw. The discharging apparatus was similar in the two, and like that already described.

There was a formidable array of rolling stock on the two sidings at the foot of the mountain where we had our car and where we camped nights. On one side track stands one of the machines, with three engines behind her; on another, the other, with the same number of locomotives. You could tell the men of the one from those of the other, for the two armies dwelt apart, just as the Denver police kept clear of the state militia in Governor Waite's war.

It was perfectly natural for the men on the different machines to be loyal to their respective employers, and a little bit jealous of the rival crew; but I was surprised to see how quickly that feeling extended to the crews of the half-dozen locomotives, all working for the same railroad company, and in no way interested in the outcome.

On the morning of the first day of the trial, when the six engines came down the track from the coal yards, a trainman stood at the three-throw switch, and gave a locomotive to each of the two machines alternately. They all knew where they belonged, and they kept the same place, each of them, until the battle was over.

There was no betting, but there was a distinct "favorite" from the start; and when the iron horses were all hooked up, the men on the "favorite" began, good-naturedly enough, to "josh" the other crew.

Mr. Egan decided that one of the machines should go forward; and when it stuck, stalled, or stopped, for any reason, it should at once back down, take the siding, and give the other a chance.

It was nearly noon when the railway officers and pencil-pushers climbed to the storm deck of the first machine, and the commander gave a signal to start. The whistle "off brakes" was answered by the six locomotives, and the little engine that brought up the rear with the special train. The hungry machine gathered up the light drifts which we encountered in the first few miles, and breathed them out over the tops of the telegraph poles. At a sharp curve, where there was a deep drift, the snowplow left the track, and we were forced to stop and back out. The engineers looked sullen as they backed down to let the other crew pass, and the fresh men laughed at them. The snow was lighter now, so that instead of boring into it, the second plow only pushed it and piled it up in front of her, until the whole house was buried, when she choked up and lay down. Now the frowns were transferred to the faces of the second crew, and smiles to the other.

For two days we seesawed in this way, and every hour the men grew more sullen. The mad locomotives seemed to enter into the spirit of the fight; at least, it was easy to imagine that they did, as they snorted, puffed, and panted in the great drifts. Ah, 'twas a goodly sight to see them, each sending an endless stream of black smoke to the very heavens, and to hear them scream to one another when about to stall, and to note with what reluctance they returned to the sidetrack.

In the little town at the foot of the hill the rival crews camped at separate boarding houses. This was fortunate, for it would not have been safe for them to live together. Even the enginemen by the end of the second day were hardly on speaking terms. Bob Stoute said that somebody had remarked that the 265 wouldn't make steam enough to ring the bell. He did not know who had said it, but he did know that he could lick him. After supper that evening, when the "scrappy" engineer came out of Red Wood's saloon, he broadened the statement so as to include "any 'Rotary' man on the job, see?"

When we went into the field on the morning of the third day, not more than seven miles of snow remained between us and the mouth of the Alpine tunnel, where the race would end, for the tunnel was full of snow. All the forenoon the hot engines steamed and snorted and banged away at the great sea of snow that grew deeper and harder as we climbed. The track was so crooked that the plows were off the rail half the time; so that when we stopped for luncheon we had made less than three miles.

The least promising of the two machines was out first after dinner; and as the snow was harder up here, she bid fair to win great credit. She rounded the last of the sharp curves that had given us so much trouble successfully.

But as the snow grew deeper she smothered, choked up, and stalled. Then even her friends had to admit that, "she was not quite right," and the enginemen looked blacker than ever as they backed down and took the siding.

Up came the rival, every engine blowing off steam, the three firemen at the furnace doors, the engineers smiling, and eager for the fray. As she turned into the tangent where the other had stalled, the leading locomotive screamed "off brakes," and every throttle flew wide open. Down, down went the reverse levers, until every engine in the train was working at her full capacity. While waiting in the siding, the engineers had screwed their "pops," or relief valves, down so that each of the engines carried twenty pounds more steam than usual. There were no drifts now, but the hard snow lay level six feet deep. The track was as good as straight—just one long curve; and the pilots would touch timberline at the mouth of the tunnel. The road here lay along the side of the mountain through a heavy growth of pine. The snow was granulated, and consequently very heavy.

By the time they had gone a hundred yards, a great stream of snow was flowing from the spout out over the telegraph wires, over the tops of the tall spruces and pines, crashing down through their branches until the white beneath them was covered with a green carpet of tree twigs. On and on, up and up, the monster moguls pushed the plow. Higher and higher rose the black smoke; and when the smoke and the snow came between the spectators and the sun, which was just now sinking behind the hill, the effect was marvelously beautiful. Still, on they went through the stainless waste, nor stopped nor stalled until the snowplow touched the tunnel shed.

The commander gave a signal to "back up"; and with faces wreathed in smiles, and with their machine covered with cinders, snow, and glory, the little army drifted down the hill. The three days' fight was at an end, and the Rotary was the victor.

But I started to write about pilot plows and old-time snow-bucking—when we used to take out an extra insurance policy and say goodbye to our friends when we signed the call-book. On a mountain division of a Western road, some ten years ago, I had my

Rotary plow pushed by helper engines, 1907.

first experience in snow-bucking. For twenty- four hours a pilot plow and flanger had been racing over the thirty miles of mountain, up one side and down the other. As often as they reached the foot of the hill they received orders to "double the road."

It was Sunday afternoon when the caller came for me. Another engine had been ordered out to help push the snowplow through the great drifts that were getting deeper and deeper every hour. Ten miles out from the division station, at the foot of the mountain proper, we sidetracked to wait the return of the snowplow.

The hours went by, the night wasted away. Monday dawned, and no news of the snow brigade. All we could learn at the telegraph office was that they were somewhere between Shawano and the top of the hill—presumably stuck in the snow. All day and all night they worked and puffed, pushed and panted, but to no purpose. Now, when they gave up all hope of getting through, they attempted to back down; but that was equally impossible. The heavy drifts in the deep cuts were not to be bucked away with the rear end of an engine.

An engine covered in snow after bucking drifts with a pilot plow, 1907.

Tuesday came, and found us still watching and waiting for the snowplow. Other engines came up from the division station with a work train, and a great army of trackmen with wide shovels. A number of railroad officers came, and everybody shoveled. We had no plow on our side of the hill, and had to buck with naked engines. First we tried one, then two, then three coupled together. The shovelers would clear off a few hundred yards of track, over which we would drive at full speed. As our engine came in contact with a great drift, all the way from eight to eighteen feet deep, she would tremble and shake as though she was about to be crushed to pieces.

Often when we came to a stop only the top of the stack of the front engine was visible. The front windows of the cabs were all boarded up to prevent the glass from being smashed. For three or four days the track was kept clear behind us, so that we could back out and tie up at night where there was coal and water. All this time the snow kept coming down, day and night, until the only sign of a railroad across the range was the tops of the telegraph poles. Toward the last of the week we encountered a terrific storm, almost a blizzard. This closed the trail behind us, and that night we were forced to camp on the mountainside. We had an abundance of coal, but the water in the tanks was very low; but by shoveling snow into them when we were stuck in deep drifts, we managed to keep them wet.

For three or four days—sometimes in the dead hours of the night—we had heard a mournful whistle away up on the mountainside, crying in the waste like a lost sheep. This was a light engine, as we learned afterward, that had started down the hill, but got stuck in the storm. For four days and nights the crews were imprisoned in the drifts. They had only a few pieces of hard bread, which they soaked in snow water and ate. More than once during the fourth day they had looked into the tallow bucket, and wondered if they could eat the tallow.

On Sunday morning, just a week from the day on which I had signed the call-book, the sun shone clear and bright. The crew with the big pilot plow had reached the summit; and now a new danger confronted the lone engine, whose cry had gone out in the night like the wail of a lost soul. The big plow was coming down the hill with two locomotives behind her; and if this crew remained on the main line, they would be scooped into eternity.

When the storm cleared away, they found that they were within a few feet of the switch target. If they could shovel out the snow and throw the switch, it would let them on to a spur. Hungry and weak as they were, they began with the fireman's scoop to clear the switch and shovel away from the wheels so that the engine could start herself. All the time they could hear the whistles of the three engines, now whistling down brakes, back up, and go ahead, as they hammered away at the deep drifts. At last the switch was forced open, the engine was in to clear; but not a moment too soon, for now came the great plow fairly falling down the mountain, sending a shower of snow over the lone engine on the spur.

We, too, had heard and seen them coming, and had found a safe siding. When the three half-starved and almost desperate engineers came to the clear track we had made, the great engines, till now held in check by the heavy snow, bounded forward down the steep grade at a rate that made us sick at heart. Each of the locomotives on the sidetrack whistled; but the wheels were covered with ice and snow, and when they reversed their engines they seemed to slide as fast. Fortunately, at the next curve, there was a heavy drift—so deep that the snow-train drove right through it, making a complete tunnel arched over with snow. Thus, after eight days, the road was opened, and eight sections of the passenger train came slowly and carefully down the mountain and passed under the arch.

Cy Warman, *Tales of an Engineer, with Rhymes of the Rail* (New York: Scribner's Sons, 1895), pp. 73-85.

THE SUPERINTENDENT AND PAWNEE BILL

Whether by means of a snowplow or a cowcatcher, the object of both was to remove obstructions from the track. The cowcatcher was a uniquely American answer to a uniquely American problem: the presence of open ranges where livestock freely roamed. After numerous incidents, a legal precedent was established that made the railroad financially responsible for killing livestock on the right-of-way. So the prudent engineer tried to avoid hitting the animals if he could possibly prevent it. Still, as related in this 1905 spoof, if he were in a hurry, and the animals weren't too big, he might get away with it—

During the winter of 1883–84, on the Evanston, Wyoming, division of the Union Pacific, it kept us quite busy keeping the road open with the old fashioned snowplows. I went out myself, and personally helped the boys to run the plow, and as Pawnee Bill had been out something like about sixty hours bucking the snow, I suggested that he go back to the caboose and get a cat nap until we reached Evanston.

I got up on the right-hand side, set the lever about two notches below the center, pulled the "bone out" (throttle full length), and never shut off for snow, livestock, or any other obstruction. The "black diamonds" were being shoveled in at a great rate by the head brakeman, who had relieved the fireman for half an hour or so, and

"Old fashioned" wedge snowplow, circa 1910.

we were sailing along about fifty miles an hour, when in rounding a curve down the hill, I noticed two cow brutes about the middle of the track.

I did not shut off, but gave the throttle another vigorous yank. Well, sir, we picked up the cattle on that plow, which was carrying tons of snow. I looked up expecting to see both animals go over the smokestack, but didn't notice it at all. I shut off, called for brakes, stopped, backed up to where we had struck the cattle, and—behold!—there they stood not over two hundred feet away, bawling, with no apparent inconvenience from their recent shock.

I got off that engine, went forward, and looked the plow over to see if it was an optical illusion. There was the imprint of both cattle in the snow on the plow. It had picked them up bodily, and set them out clear, absolutely uninjured.

Pawnee Bill, the half-breed engineer, got one on me later. It was on the same division, and after the snow had all gone in the spring of the year. Bill was going west on train 7, and ran into a band of sheep, killing seventy-eight head, but never made any report of it.

The owner of the herd had Tim Coonrod make a special report. Tim was section foreman at that point on the line, and the section house was only a few hundred yards from where the sheep were killed.

Tim said to me: "Personally, Misther Dickinson, I saw thim wid me own oiyes. That haythen injun who runs injine two twinty-siven, Pawnee Bill, came by about foive a.m. in the mornin' as Oi wus tellin' you before in me lether of explanation. Oi saw the whole thing as plin as the nose on me face. Oi saw Pawnee Bill run schmack into thim and the whole country round had shape to ate fer at least a munth."

"Well," said I to Tim, "you remain here, and I'll send the call-boy down to the roundhouse and bring Bill up here, and we'll have this thing straightened out.

Showing off her rakish cowcatcher, this is Chicago & Northwestern engine 605 at Tracy, Minnesota, circa 1890.

Bill came in, and I began to interrogate him again about having killed those sheep. He said: "Why, Mr. Dickinson, I never killed any sheep."

He had not noticed Tim in the corner until I spoke and asked him to please relate, for Mr. Pawnee Bill's benefit, what he had seen on that morning.

Tim, at my request, related the whole incident, as he remembered it.

I noticed Bill's face grow very red before Tim had finished—his black eyes flashing like coals of fire, and his mind seemed to be conjuring up some mode of escape. Tim had finished.

"Well, Bill," I said, "how about it?"

"Well, Mr. Dickinson, I guess you have got me cornered, and I'll have to tell the truth.

"I did strike 'em, but hit 'em so d—d hard that I did not suppose any of 'em had yet time to come down out of the clouds."

S.T. Sallee, "My Old Superintendent and Pawnee Bill," *The Railway Conductor* 22, no. 3 (March 1905): 170-71.

ONLY A SWITCHMAN

A link-and-pin coupler.

Prior to 1900, most railroads used the dangerous link-and-pin coupler on freight cars. This simple device consisted of a heavy, elongated loop—similar to a chain link—that fit into the coupler box on either end of a car. The link was secured with a large-diameter pin that dropped down though the coupler box and link.

The problem was that the link had to be held horizontally when two cars came together for a coupling. If a switchman's hand wasn't removed at the last instant, it would be mashed between the coupler boxes. And sometimes the cars coupled so closely to one another that a switchman could be crushed between them.

Add to this the constant hazard of stepping over and around switch points and stubs, as well as dodging moving cars and riding on their roofs—often accomplished at night in an unlighted freight yard—and one begins to sense the peril of the job.

*This danger was not lost on a Chicago newspaper reporter who, in 1893, quite aptly captured the essence of it in her factual story, entitled... **Only a Switchman.***

Eight hundred thousand men find employment on the various railroad lines which traverse the United States, and of these fully one-fourth are stationed in the yards as switchmen. Of all the men who have anything to do with railroading there are none of which the public know so little as switchmen. Did you ever notice the one-armed, one-legged man waving his red flag at the crossing? He is known as a flagman but he was a switchman once, and there are many hundreds of others just like him.

Did you ever see a one-armed man struggling with the patent lock of a switch, his empty sleeve fluttering in the wind? He is only tending switches now, but he once belonged to a switch crew, rode on an engine and helped to make up the long trains which carried passengers and freight out of Chicago.

It's a dangerous calling—this occupation of switchman, with meager chance of promotion and little recognition by the public, but it is a necessary and important one. They are as much a part of the road as the conductor, who takes charge of the train after it is made up, or the engineer who pulls it, and without them trains would stop, roads would become blocked, and traffic finally cease altogether.

More than two thousand men are employed in this capacity in the yards about Chicago, and their happy, easy manner, the "come-

Yard switchmen, such as the one walking the car top in the left center, had to develop a keen sense of balance, or else. Chicago, 1906.

a-day, go-a-day" expression which seems to find a permanent resting place on their bronzed faces would lead one to believe that they had the best time in the world—a downhill pull on life, as it were. They are a rough, healthy, hard-working, honest crowd, and the heavy outdoor employment has given them the brawny, well-knit frames of Roman gladiators.

No one can fully understand the multifarious duties which fall to the lot of switchmen without paying a visit to some one of the many yards. In and out, over and under the moving train, waving their arms and shouting to the engineers, apparently with as little thought of their perilous position as a man on an ox cart, a happy lot, who seem too busy to let the cares of life worry them for a moment. The switchman's work is not all manual labor, though it is rough and dirty. He must be cool and quick of action at critical moments; he must have a perfect conception of force and distance and be conversant with the time cards of all the roads, for those in charge of the transfer trains often visit two or three yards during the day and must give right of way to regular trains.

From 7 o'clock at night to 6 o'clock in the morning is the busiest time in the yard. Then they are making up the trains for next day. All night long the engines puff and sputter and throw myriads of sparks from their stacks, dropping a car here and one there, like a mail clerk distributing letters, until the engines stand alone exhausting steam as if tired out with work.

At night, too, the switchmen must be more careful. They must be ever on the watch lest a misstep throw them in the way of a moving car, resulting in the loss of a limb, or what is still more serious, life. Of the 28,000 employees killed and injured on the railroad the past year fully one-third met with the accident while coupling or uncoupling cars. Statistics show that one man in every thirty who follows railroading meets with an accident, and the chances are about equal when one does occur that the unfortunate is a switchman.

In a law recently passed by the legislature compelling railroads to equip their rolling stock with automatic brakes and couplers the switchmen have some hope of lightening their labors and removing the possibility of accident. This will also tend to reduce the rate of insurance, a $500 policy being the most any company will take, and for which they charge the extortionate premium of $37.

An engineer, fireman, foreman, and two helpers constitute a switch crew, unless there is a grade, in which case two extra helpers are carried. When hired by the month they receive a salary of from $65 to $70, ten hours constituting a day, though they not infrequently work extra time when trains are late or the yards blocked. No regular hour is set for dinner and they are compelled to eat at odd moments wherever they happen to be.

Fraught with danger even greater than that of the soldier who goes to battle, beset on every side by responsibility for the safety of lives and freight, the switchman is rarely recognized by the public as an important part of a great railroad system.

The passengers seated in the luxurious apartments of a palace car, spinning across the country toward Chicago at the rate of 60 miles an hour, over a well packed roadbed and a straight track, is apt, in these days of railroad perfection, to give little thought to the possibility of an accident. Yet as the train nears the yards with its network of tracks, thickly dotted with the red, green, and white lights, and he sees the fierce glare of the headlights of a dozen puffing engines, the waving to and fro of the workmen's lanterns and the swiftly moving trains, though ever so slightly conversant with the railroad system, he cannot but seriously contemplate the imminent danger from a misplaced switch or a confusion of signals and feel a trifle uneasy until the train sets its brakes under the great canopy of the station. And yet the switchman's hand is not recognized in this.

Tony Eckart, "Only a Switchman," *Switchman's Journal* 8, no. 1 (May 1893): 17-19.

WHEN THE TEXAN
WAS YARDMASTER

There were other kinds of hazards in a switchyard. Sometimes the freight itself could pose a threat. Take, for instance, the hauling of livestock. Shipping cattle was a routine matter for the western railroads. At certain times of the year in Kansas, where our next story is set, shipments of live cattle headed to the meat packing houses in Kansas City or Chicago outnumbered all other manifests.

*Most of these bovines were Texas Longhorns, a particularly ill-mannered breed whose name was no exaggeration. One look at those six-foot wide antlers would convince anyone that these steers were not to be trifled with. But as long as they were penned in the cattle cars or loading chutes, all was well. The trouble is that sometimes they didn't take kindly to such cramped quarters. And, the world being what it is, things don't always go as they are supposed to, such as **When the Texan Was Yardmaster**.*

After "Windy" Walker, fireman, had flourished the scoop shovel on the Pollywog branch passenger run several years, the division foreman gave him a job running a switch engine preparatory to an examination for engineer.

It took "Windy" to tell stories. In fact, to that talent he owed the significant sobriquet, "Windy." And after "Windy" took the switch engine job, his association with the switchmen was, of itself, a good reason for enhancing his accomplishment of exaggerating facts until they wouldn't recognize their own proportions.

One of the deals that made "Windy" Walker a friend of the switchmen was once when he relieved them of the uncomfortable and necessarily dangerous positions of imitating a gang of Spanish bullfighters. The details of the excitement in the yards the morning a raw-boned, red-eyed, long-horned Texas steer impudently assumed the responsibilities of yardmaster, certainly make a thrilling story, and as Walker was the hero of the day, it is only just dues that, whenever anyone wants to hear about what the Texan stirred up, the switchmen would call in "Windy," and tell him to loosen up his vocabulary.

"Well," hesitated "Windy," in relating the tale about when the Texas steer ran riot in the yards, "about the first thing that impressed me that morning was that when a man gets his wits balled up good and big, his hair really does stand on end.

"We had a brawny, rough-necked Irishman, named O'Harrety, slamming switch stands in the east end, and the first thing I saw of that long-horned Texas skeleton, was when O'Harrety came down the line along a string of boxcars on 'six' track, at a scared-to-death pace. That Irishman had an elaborate flow of Irish-English when he wasn't flustered, but laboring under excitement, O'Harrety's tongue had nervous prostration. One would have reckoned the devil and all his hired men were on that Irishman's trail. His hair looked like the bristles on a curry-comb, and he was wavin' his hat and yellin' loud enough to wake up a cemetery. The gang about the shanty door naturally got curious, and began rubberin' in O'Harrety's direction, and all of a sudden, when that pale Irishman was about close enough for us to whistle down brakes, so he could make an explanation as to why he was overdoin' the yard speed rate of six miles an hour, we got the first glimpse of a Texas steer, all horns and two weary

Rail facilities adjacent to the Kansas City stockyards, 1909.

eyes, as he swung around the corner of the nearest string of cars, and headed down the lead for the shanty. The way we fellers helter-skeltered into that switch shanty wasn't at all slow.

"O'Harrety was a few lengths in th' lead of the steer, and when I seen he was makin' a beeline for the door, I stood inside and held it part way open for him. That Irishman didn't stop at the door, either. He sort a-tripped on the sill, and his speed was geared so high that he landed like a chunk of mud up against the opposite wall, then fell onto the bench along the wall with a groanin' breath that sounded like his safety valve had popped open and he was just puffin' out excess power. 'Course, I slammed the door shut, so that mean-looking Texan wouldn't take a notion to follow.

"But, talk about your head-end collisions! I have been in one or two myself, but they was just little love-taps. That cussed steer made a header for that shanty door—nothin' could stop him. I, like the rest of the fellows, was laughin' at the scared Irishman, when, whop! Somethin' landed up against that door. I thought mebby it was a runaway engine. Y'see, I was tryin' to hold the door shut, and that swat jarred me up hard enough to give my great-great-grandfather the shaking palsy. That old door went to pieces so fast I couldn't keep track of the pieces. Tell you, about that time I wasn't able to keep track of myself. I think I must have hit the ceilin'. Anyhow, I came down across the top of the stove with part of the stovepipe gracefully wrapped about my neck. I didn't stop to see how many cracked ribs I had or whether the stove was worst hurt than I was, but after the stars and stripes had cleared off the right of way of my eyesight, I saw at a glance a pair of feet disappearing out each window, and that I was alone in the cabin.

"But imagine my state of mind when I looked around and saw there in the doorway, the countenance of that wild-eyed rack-o'-bones, hind hoofs up in the air and front ones pawin' dirt all over the railroad track, a-figurin' how to get a pair of six-foot horns through a three-foot wide doorway. Thank goodness, that old boy's geometry was a slow process sort, and by the time he had figured out what angle to slant his horns to get inside, I had followed O'Harrety through the open window. I made my getaway in such a hurry, that I probably would have plowed a furrow through the cinders with my chin, if I hadn't a-lit head first on O'Harrety's breadbasket.

It like to winded him, but without dallyin' to see whether he had lost his breath, false teeth, watch, head, or any other staple and fancy valuables, we hiked off to my engine which was standin' in front of the shanty; and after I was up in the cab, I wasn't dead certain that steer wasn't followin' me till I heard him bawlin' and scatterin' destruction inside the shanty. He got inside, all right. 'Spect he thought it was terribly impolite of us not to 've been there to receive our guest, so he took his vengeance out on the furniture, which was a mighty hard matter to get satisfaction out of, I'll bet.

"The Texan finished dilapidatin' the stove, incidentally slashed the points of his hookers through all the window lights of the establishment and when he stalked out of the door, he carried the back of a busted chair on one horn, and from the tip of the other,

A cattle car. From *The Car Builders Dictionary*, **1895.**

jauntily suspended by its wire hanger, was a picture of an actress, a theatre poster that one of the switchmen had framed and hung up in the shanty.

"About that time we began spreadin' the alarm and wonderin' how many partners he had runnin' at large, but he seemed to be the only Texan out. It was along in the spring of the year, when the shipments of Texas cattle to Kansas ranges are pretty numerous, and we sort o' decided that that murderous-lookin' pair of horns must have escaped from some cattle car, by crawlin' through the slats, and that steer was certainly bony enough to.

I'd always heard that when a genuine Texas steer, and especially a hungry one, gets on the war path, he goes plum crazy, and the insane asylum was certainly the only place for that wild-eyed beast. Tell y' what, that critter was on a man hunt. He paraded about the yards and every time he caught sight of a switchman, or anyone else, for that matter, the dirt began to fly. The switchmen did the Spanish bullfighter act to a finish. Their chief getaway when the green-eyed monster made an unexpected sally on them was to dodge in between the ends of two boxcars. When the cars are in a train you know there is a space between them of about eighteen inches, and the steer couldn't get to 'em. But he would smash up against the cars, though, if he could not hit the switchmen. He wouldn' stop at nothing. If a feller would dodge behind a stone wall, I guess he'd just as soon plunk into the stone wall as the pine door of that old switch shanty.

"Well, the rascal slam-banged around there until he had a corner on the switchman market. Anyhow, he had all the switchmen cornered. Things began gettin' in pretty bad shape. The yards were gettin' blocked. The freight trains kept pullin' in until there were no tracks to hold them and no trains were bein' made up to amount to anything.

"Switchman O'Harrety's individual excitement had reached such high pressure that he was architect for some mighty reckless, daredevil plans. He got a rope from somewhere; said he used to be somewhat of a cowboy himself, and would see if throwin' a lasso was a lost art to him. Well, he had the good luck to 'get next' real soon. He spied the steer coming down alongside a string of boxcars, so he gets on top of a car and waits cautious-like till the steer comes along. As soon as he had passed a little ways, O'Harrety drops the loop over one horn and then braces himself for trouble. The funny thing about it was that just about that time, that wanderin' skeleton caught sight of a blue-shirted switchman, a few car lengths away, who had got interested in O'Harrety's scheme and stepped out in the open to watch results, and they certainly were worth watchin'.

"'Course, the steer was up on his toes after that blue shirt, straight away, and was makin' about three hundred revolutions a minute when he got to the end of the rope. All of a sudden it became taut. Before it happened, O'Harrety saw there would be somethin' doin', and he took an extra brace for the recoil, lay back on the lasso for dear life. And for about a minute, I guess, he wondered whether he had any dear life or not. He was jerked off that car for about two full, regulation-sized somersaults towards the steer, and at the same time, the steer threw the reverser and made a backward flip-flop in the air. Fortunately O'Harrety didn't light very hard in his acrobatic stunt off the boxcar. When he and the steer regained their equilibrium, they came up face to face only a few feet apart. I don't know which was frightened the worst, but I think the steer was. They looked blankly at each other for a second, as if wonderin' how it all happened, and the beast bawled out a bum note, whirled about and started after the blue shirt he had his lookers on before that sudden interruption.

"The Irishman was glued onto that rope, though, and the steer soon discovered that its energy was in the wrong direction, so again he wheeled about, and charged on O'Harrety. Old Ireland seemed to think it was a foregone conclusion that the two ends of the rope had to pull in opposite directions, and when he saw the steer with pilot pointin' his way, head down, and tail over the dashboard, he just stood there as though waitin' for someone to wave a red light before he could smell danger. That Irishman had stage fright. He bunched his wits, though, soon enough to head in under a boxcar, just in time to fight shy of that pair of vicious snags. O'Harrety decided lassoin' wasn't just exactly his profession, and gave it up.

"Only one fellow was caved in by that wild-eyed Texan that mornin', and it made a selection that pleased the switchmen mighty much. You remember old Webb Moore, that brass-voiced, brow-beatin' extract of humanity? Well, he was yardmaster then. He happened to look out over the yards from his office window and saw the yards were blocked up pretty badly. He threw a fit and came chasin' down the line, bawlin' half as loud as the old steer was. When he saw what was up, he meandered over to where the gang was and wanted to know what in the deuce the yards were all blocked up for. He found out mighty soon, too. 'Lord' Moore thought it a shame that a lot of men should be buffaloed, scared from duty by as frail a lookin' specimen as that old Texas ranger, so he started in to 'shoo' the longhorn off the premises, just like an old woman would charge down on a flock of chickens if they were scratchin' in her flowerbed.

"But the steer didn't 'shoo.' Moore made a bold dash at first, but when he saw the critter didn't take to the timber, he slackened his pace. The steer just kind o' watched him out of the corners of his wild-lookin' optics until Moore got pretty close. Then all in a jiffy that four-footed stranger let out a vicious bawl and went through the air with the throttle wide open. Moore didn't more 'an get turned around, than the steer landed on his 'dead wood,' and I'll be jostled if his majesty, the yardmaster, didn't roll about twenty feet, and after he had reached a slowdown, he had sense enough to roll himself over a time or two more, which put him out of reach of the steer, in under a boxcar. And if he hadn't a-gotten under the boxcar, it certainly would have been time for the accident insurance man to come 'round, for that animule just kept right after him. When he saw he couldn't touch him, Mr. Steer moseyed on down the track with blood in his eye, still lookin' for big game.

"Well, the bunt that cactus-fed steer shoved onto 'Lord' Moore, certainly took a few kinks out of his self-respect. The switchmen felt like passin' the hat to buy the old steer a bucket of bran, but, of course, they couldn't afford to give way on their sentiments like that. As soon as Moore had coupled himself together, he crawled out from under that car and swore vengeance. The switchmen could not help givin' him the horse laugh about shooin' away the steer, and he couldn't hold back from grinnin' right foolish-like all the time he was belchin' out cuss words big enough to wreck a train.

"Moore went straight to a restaurant not far off and borrowed a Winchester rifle; said he would sure clean up for that brute. He dodged about among the boxcars until he got a good bead on the steer. And just about that time the steer got a bead on the yardmaster. Moore up and blazed away. He never touched the steer, but the bullet whispered somethin' in a switchman's ear a few car lengths away, and brought out a powerfully bold stream of cuss words about what a fool the yardmaster was. The yardmaster, though, about that time was engaged in other pursuits than listenin' to a loud-mouthed switchman; good thing for the switchman's standin' with the company that he didn't hear, too. Moore blazed away a second time at the string of bones bearin' down on him. I don't believe the yardmaster could hit a flock of barns, let alone that steer, 'cause it was built on the nar-raw gauge plan and when comin' straight at a fellow it was just like shootin' at a string. Of course, the second shot went wild. It was about time for a bayonet charge or to swing clubbed muskets, but Moore, in a very hasty manner, laid aside his arms and was in full retreat. It certainly was another Bull Run, or steer-run, as you like it. Moore managed to find a timely life-savin'station between the ends of two boxcars.

"I had gotten a-thunderin' lot of amusement out of this wild animal show and kind o' hated to spoil the fun, but it looked like somethin' had to be done. Excitement was rife about the place and there was mighty little work bein' done. A lot of shop men were up on top of the roundhouse, takin' a bird's- eye view of the maneuvers, and the men from the freight house, wonderin' why the switchmen hadn't brought some freight cars down to the platform to empty, had come down to the yards to find out what the agitation was and were lined up on some boxcars watchin' the fun. Someone phoned uptown for a policeman—but, of course, a copper wasn't expected to show up on the scene of action till several hours after the trouble was all over—thinkin' the cop might have a right to shoot the steer for raisin' hell without a city license, you know. Anyhow, somethin'had to be done, and a happy thought struck me. That walleyed ox was standin' in the middle of 'eight' track and the right of way was clear from my end of the yards to the steer. So I tells one of the switchmen to let me in on 'eight' track and I would run down on the critter and put him out of business.

"I was sort o' anxious to see what the steer would do when he saw a steam engine prancin' down on him. I pulled the whistle string and when the Texan heard the toot, toot, and spied the engine comin', he just reared up on his hind feet and tore up the dirt like a steam shovel. The critter was certainly lookin' for as big game as he could see, and was immensely delighted at the thought of a challenge from the iron hoss; so here he comes just a-flyin' and a-bellerin'. I loosened up the throttle a little bit till I was hittin' a pretty good lick, because the only thing to do in my estimation was to bust the brute's neck, so I went after him for blood.

"There was a head-end collision like them you read about. Talk about the cow jumpin' over the moon! You ought to have got a glimpse of the mid-air tour that Texas steer took. I heard that wiry old neck snap like a brittle saplin', and his carcass streaked out like it had wings; went plum over some boxcars on the next track and lit on the cinders limp as a rag.

"But to give the devil his dues, I must say that raw-boned critter put up a good battle. He got in a sort of a side lick on the pilot of my engine that put the pony trucks clean off the rails, and after we had bounced over a few rail lengths of ties and tore up three or four rails, I managed to reach a standstill. I left the engine to the mercy of the yard gang and they had her back on the track in a little while.

"The switchmen wanted to give me three cheers and a tiger for the good riddance of bad rubbish. The steer was dead after about three or four hours of delay, but the yard work was soon on full blast again.

"I never did feel that I got my money's worth out of that deal, though. I'll admit it was a circus and was worth considerable, but it cost me just $30 out of my next pay check. Why, you know the

End of the line for these Texas Longhorns. The Chicago stockyards, 1900.

claim agent was around a day or two later and informed me the owner of that steer wanted the money for it, and said it was up to me to muster up my small change. I couldn't see it that way, but he changed my train of vision along that line, however. Told me I voluntarily ran down the steer; had me where I couldn't back out, so I signed up for the damages, and posted that thirty plunks on the losin' side of my account book to 'popular amusements.'"

E.W. Swan, "When the Texan was Yardmaster," *Along the Line; or, Western Railroad Stories* (New York: Broadway Publishing, 1905): 31-44.

THE LAP ORDER

Railroad operations have grown safer over the years. But it has come with a price. Nearly every new innovation, be it in signaling, communications, or dispatching, has been the result of a horrible mistake or terrible tragedy that amplified the need for a better way of doing things.

In the 1890s railroads relied on a system known as timetable and train order to control the movement of trains over a single track. Under that system, late trains or extra trains were subject to telegraphic orders from the dispatcher for safe movement from one passing siding to the next. Automatic trackside signals were still in the future for most railroads, and manually operated signals depended on the dispatcher's orders or established rules.

Essentially, there was no backup method if the dispatcher erred or the train crew misread or forgot an order.

*The term "lap order" was something no one wanted to hear. It referred to the dispatcher's worst nightmare, an overlapping of orders. It meant that two trains were going to meet, head-on, due to a dispatcher's mistake—and there was no **earthly** way to stop them…*

I do not believe that Stevenson ever had an enemy. A right clever engineer he was, with always a good word, even under no end of pressure. Which is saying a good deal, when speaking of engineers in general. Fast as he climbed, his head never swelled. But his heart grew right along after his head stopped, and that's where he laid over some other engineers I could mention if I had to, which I don't—at least not here.

Our story opens in the fall of 1893. Stevenson was then running a ten-wheeler, on one of the Exposition Flyers. He was due to arrive at Pine Creek Siding at 10:50 p.m., and would ordinarily have met his opposing train at Runton, which is a good bit west of the river. But his engine had been steaming badly all the way from Pinto, and on her schedule, which was crazy fast all night, she did not reach Pine Creek till some fifty minutes late.

Preparations had been made on the division to help Stevenson, when news floated in to the dispatchers' office, that an engineer of a big ten-wheeler, pulling twenty-five cars of steers, had been pushing hard, and at the entrance of the cut, twelve miles east, set his air so quick he sprung one of the driver shoes and the main rod hit it. The great steel bar doubled up like a man with the cramps. There was a bright vmoon; they made a stop, and as quick as men could do it, flagged both ways. Here an added forty-five minutes gave Stevenson an opportunity to do some very tall running.

It was exactly 10 p. m. when I walked into the dispatcher's office. The lights in the yard were low and the freshening winds had driven the clouds from the sky, in which a brilliant moon hung like a disk of silver. Upstairs every door was locked and every room was dark, except the dispatcher's office. In that room Allen sat at his key;

A high-drivered ten-wheeler of the Rock Island Railroad, circa 1893.

near by, but closer to the stove, sat the night caller, trying to starch his hair with a ten cent novel. As I walked in, Allen raised his eyes, "Trouble at Pine Creek. Extra 642 has thrown a rod. Stevenson is behind him," he said, resuming his grasp of the key.

Now between Pine Creek and Pinto, twenty miles apart, there are two sidings, Pilot Knob, west of the river, and Indian Head, east. There was no operator at either place and the train that leaves Pine Creek, westbound, is in the open for twenty miles with only schedule rights, or an operator's tissue between them, and the worst of it.

When the muss at Pine Creek had been cleared and Stevenson was again on his way, Allen set about making new meeting points for him and No. 12. At exactly 11:15 p.m., he wired an order to Pine Creek for No. 12 to hold at Pilot Knob for No. 1 (Stevenson). A minute later he sent an order for No. 1 to run to Pine Creek, regardless of No. 12.

When he had made the meeting point, Allen rose from his chair and sat down by the stove. I lazily watched him till, falling into a doze as I eyed him drowsily, he began to loom up in his chair and to curl and twist toward the roof like a signal column; then the front legs of his chair struck the floor, and with a start I woke, just as he stepped hurriedly back to his table and picked up the order book. The first suspicion that I had that anything was wrong, was an exclamation from Allen as he stared at the book. Putting it down almost at once, he plugged McGowan's house wire, and began drumming his call. "I, I," came back inside of a moment, and Allen tapped right back at him, "Come down," and I began to wonder what was up. The sounder broke and he turned back, listened a moment; but it was stray stuff about time freight; he pushed the chair from behind him, still like a man listening—listening; then with an effort, plain even to me, he walked across the office, pushed open the door of McGowan's private office, and stood with his hand on the knob, looking back at the lamp; it was as if he still seemed to listen, for he stood undecided a moment, then he stepped into the dark room and closed the door behind him, leaving me alone and dumb with fear.

The mystery I knew lay in the order book. Curiosity gradually got the better of my fright, and I crossed over to the dispatcher's table where the train order book was lying, open, where he had left it, under the lamp. With my eyes bulging, I read the last two orders copied in it:

C&E No. 12, Pine Creek. No. 12, Eng. 1022, will hold at Pilot Knob, for No. 1.

No. 1, Eng. 916, will run to Pine Creek, regardless of No. 12.— M.M.

Pine Creek. I glared at the words and the letters of the words. I re-read the first order, and read again the second. Pilot Knob for No. 12, that was all right. Pilot Knob it should be for No. 1, but it wasn't; it was the first station east of Pilot Knob he had ordered Stevenson to run to. It was a lap order. My scalp began to creep. My mouth went sticking dry. The horror of the impending wreck through his mistake began to grow on me; I know what I suffered; I ask myself what he suffered, inside alone in the dark. Oh, you who lie down upon the rail at night to sleep, in a dispatcher's hand, think you ever in your darkened berths of the cruel responsibility on the man who in the watches of the night, holds you in his keeping? Others may blunder, others may forget; others may fall and stand again; not the dispatcher; a single mistake damns him. We he falls he falls forever.

McGowan's door opened again and Allen came out of the dark. He looked at me eagerly; the expression of his face had completely changed. I never in my life saw such a change in so few minutes on any man's face, and, like all the rest, it alarmed me. He walked over to the table and plugging McGowan's house wire again, sent just these words, "You need not come down." He glanced vacantly around; seemed for the first time to see me.

"Is there anything that I can do?" I faltered. Even if the words meant nothing, the offer must have touched him.

"No, Fred," he answered quietly, "there isn't." With the words the hall door opened, and McGowan, in his ulster, threw it wide open and stood facing us both.

"Is anything wrong?" he asked with anxiety restrained in his tone.

"Yes, something serious has happened. I have sent lap orders to Nos. 1 and 12. Instead of making a meeting point at Pilot Knob, I sent 12 an order to run to Pilot Knob, and ordered 1 to run to Pine Creek against her."

"What have you done to meet it? Where's your wreckers? Where's your relief? What are you doing? Nothing? Why don't you speak? Will you kill two train loads of people without an effort to do anything?" Mac's voice rang absolute terror to me. "Be a man; say something!"

"Mac, there'll be no wreck," he answered steadily.

"Be no wreck?" thundered McGowan. "Be no wreck? Two passenger trains meet head on and be no wreck? Are you crazy?"

The dispatcher's hands clutched at the table. "No," he persisted steadily, "I am not crazy. Don't make me so. I tell you there will be no wreck."

"Allen, if you are sane, I don't know what you mean. Don't stand there like that. Do you know what you have done?"

"Mac," he struggled, putting out his hand toward the night chief, "I am sure of what I say. There will be no wreck. When I saw what I had done—knew it was too late to undo it—I begged God that my hands might not be stained with their blood. I was answered," he exclaimed with a strange confidence. "I saw Stevenson, and he said there would be no wreck; I cannot see what will happen. I do not know what; but there will be no wreck. Believe me or not—it is so."

Allen's steadfast manner staggered the chief. I could imagine what he was debating as he looked at Allen—wondering, maybe, whether the man's mind had gone. Mac was staggered; he looked it, as he collected himself to speak again. Before he could, however, the hall door opened like an uncanny thing, and the superintendent burst in upon us. "What's so?" he echoed. "What's up here? There's been trouble, hasn't there? What's the matter with you all? Mac, is everybody struck dumb?"

The chief spoke, "There's a lap order out on 1 and 12. We don't know what's happened," he answered sullenly. "Allen has gone crazy—or he knows—somehow—says he has seen Stevenson in a vision; and there won't be any wreck. It's between Pine Creek and Pilot Knob, somewhere."

The superintendent looked around. "Gentlemen, what does this mean? Somebody here is insane. I want to hear it all." The chief put up a hand, and without a word of comment repeated Allen's story just as the dispatcher had told it. "In any event there's nothing to do now; it's on us or we're past it. Let us wait for No. 1 to report."

In the meantime Stevenson had got around the wreck. The orders in his pocket gave No. 1 a free sweep to Pine Creek, and Stevenson was the man to take it good and hard. How he climbed the mountains and skirted the river banks, and crawled down two and three percent grades; and the time it took him to do it, is now a subject of conversation. The 916 never behaved better. The olive green string—from tender to tail lights—seemed to move with the grace of a proud woman. And the time that Stevenson made that night, when one hour and fifty-five minutes late, caused everyone to look upon him with awe.

Back in the dispatcher's office the superintendent was pacing the floor. Mac stuck silent to the key, taking what little work came, for I saw neither of them cared to trust Allen at the key. McGowan had the orders repeated from Pine Creek and Pinto, and they were as Allen had said; they did lap; they had been sent just as the order book showed. There was nothing for it but to wait for Pine Creek to hear from No. 1.

When the night operator there called the dispatcher again it brought Allen out of his gloom like a thunder clap. "Give me the key," he exclaimed, "there is Pine Creek."

McGowan pushed back, and Allen dropping into the chair, took the message from the night operator at Pine Creek: "No. 1 in at 11:20 p.m."

Allen answered him, and strangely, with all the easy confidence of his ordinary sending. "Ask Stevenson to come to the wire," he sent to Pine Creek.

"Engineer Stevenson here," came back.

"Ask Stevenson where he met No. 12 tonight."

We waited, wrought up, for us that reply must come the answer to all this mystery. There was a hitch at the other end of the wire; then Pine Creek answered: "Stevenson says he will tell you all about it in the morning."

"That will not do," tapped back the dispatcher. "This is Allen; Superintendent Ketchum and McGowan are here. They want the facts. Where did you meet No. 12?"

There was another wearing delay, then the answer came slowly, at the engineer's dictation:

"My orders at Indian Head, read, 'Run to Pine Creek regardless of No. 12.' When I cleared Pinto and got down to the bottom of the long fill, I was cutting it off pretty hard to make the rise, when I saw, or thought I saw, a headlight flash between the Twin Sisters, at the end of the ten mile stretch. It startled me, for I knew that No. 12 could not be very far west of us. Anyway I made a quick stop, and reversing, backed tight as I could make it for the siding at Indian Head. Before I had got a mile back, I saw the headlight again, and I knew that was 12, against our order. We got into clear just as 12 went by a-humming. Nobody but our train crew and my fireman knows anything about this."

At this point Pine Creek closed the key. The three men in front of me made no comment as they looked at each other.

Allen, getting up, steadied himself on his feet. "Go in there and lie down," said McGowan, "you're all used up. Don't say a word about this."

"Not a word," put in the Superintendent, resting his hand on the dispatcher's shoulder. "There's no harm done; nobody knows it. Bury the thing right here, tonight. You're broke up; go in there and lie down."

He took their hands; started to speak; but they pushed him into McGowan's room; they didn't want to hear anything. Gradually the office grew quiet. And in the morning when McGowan went to call Allen he found him face down on the floor. In his hands, clasped tight, they found his watch with the picture of his wife and baby.

Had he asked, when first he went into that room that night— when he wrestled in his agony of prayer—that his life be taken if only their lives—the lives of those in his keeping, might be spared? I do not know. They found him dead.

Frederick A. Starges, "The Lap Order," *The Railway Conductor* 23, no. 6 (June 1906): 423-26.

THE NIGHT DISPATCHER

The name of Frank L. Packard is not too well known these days. More's the pity because the Canadian-born Packard (1877–1942) was a prolific novelist and short story writer who specialized in mysteries and railroad themes. His writings were so popular that at least two of his works were made into movies in the silent film era.

Packard drew upon his turn-of-the-century experience as a civil engineer with the Canadian Pacific Railway to create a series of stories about railroading through Rockies on the fictional Hill Division. The selection below, from 1910, is another story of a dispatcher in trouble, but with a different twist, and told in Packard's unique style. It was one of his earlier successes and it serves well as a sampling of his more than one hundred short stories that would follow—

East and west now the Transcontinental is double-tracked, all except the Hill Division—and that, in the nature of things, probably never will be. If you know the mountains, you know the Hill Division. From the divisional point, Big Cloud, that snuggles at the eastern foothills, the right of way, like the trail of a great sinewy serpent, twists and curves through the mountains, through the Rockies, through the Sierras, and finally emerges to link its steel with a sister division that stretches onward to the great blue of the Pacific Ocean.

**Single track mountain railroading—a succession of cuts and fills—
with no room for error. Utah, 1914.**

It is a stupendous piece of track. It has cost fabulous sums and
the lives of many men; it has made the fame of some, and been the
graveyard of more. The history of the world—in big things, in little
things, in battles, in strife, in sudden death, in peace, in progress,
and in achievement—has its counterpart in miniature in the history
of the Hill Division. There is a page in that history that belongs to
"Angel" Breen. This is Breen's story:

It has been written much, and said oftener, that men in every
walk of life, save one, may make mistakes and live them down, but
that the dispatcher who falls once is damned forever. And it is true.
I am a dispatcher. I know.

Where he got the nickname "Angel" from is more than I can tell,
and I've wondered at it often enough myself. Contrast, I guess it was.
Contrast with the boisterous, rough-and-ready men around him, for

this happened back in the early days when men were what a life of hardship and no comfort made them. No, Breen wasn't soft—far from it. He was just quiet and mild-mannered. It must have been that—contrast. Anyway, he was "Angel" when I first knew him, and you can draw your own conclusion as to what he is now—I'm not saying anything at all about that.

Where did he come from? What was he before he came here? I don't believe anybody knew or ever gave the matter a thought. That sort of question was never asked—it was too delicate and pointed in the majority of cases. A man was what he was out here, not what he had been; he made good, or he didn't. Not that I mean to imply that there was anything crooked or anything wrong with Breen's past; I'm sure there wasn't, for that matter; but I'm just trying to make you understand that when I say Breen had the night trick in the dispatcher's office here in Big Cloud I'm beginning at the beginning.

Breen wasn't popular. He wasn't a good enough mixer for that. Personally, it isn't anything I'd hold up against him or any other man. Popularity is too often cheap, and a "good fellow" isn't always a license for a man to puff out his chest—though most of them do it, and that's the high sign that what I say is right. No, I'm not moralizing; I'm telling a story; you'll see what I mean before I get through. I say Breen wasn't popular. He got the reputation of thinking himself a little above the rank and file of those around him—stuck-up, to put it in cold English, and that's where they did him an injustice. It was the man's nature, unobtrusive, retiring—different from theirs, if you get my point, and they couldn't understand, just because it was different. The limitations weren't all up to Breen.

If they had known, or taken the trouble to know, as much about him as they could have known, before passing judgment on him, perhaps things might have been a little different; perhaps not. I won't say, for it's pretty generally accepted in railroad law that a dispatcher's slip is a capital offense, and there's no court of appeal, no stay of execution, no anything, and to all intents and purposes he's dead from the moment that slip is made.

There have been lots of cases like that—lots of them—and there's no class of men I pity more—a slip, and damned for the rest of their lives! I don't say that because I'm a dispatcher myself. We're only human, aren't we? Mistakes like that, God knows, aren't made intentionally. Sometimes a man is overworked, sometimes queer brain kinks happen to him just as they do to every other man. We're ranked as humans in everything but our work.

I'm not saying it's not right. In the last analysis I suppose it has to be that way. It's part of the game, and we know the rules when we "sit in." We've no reason to complain, only I get a shiver every time I read a newspaper headline that I know, besides being a death warrant, is tearing the heart out of some poor devil. You've seen the kind I mean, read scores of them— "Dispatcher's Blunder Costs Many Lives"—or something to the same effect. Maybe you'll think it queer, but for days afterward I can't handle an order book or a train sheet when I'm on duty without my heart being in my mouth half of the time.

What's this got to do with Breen? Well, in one way, it hasn't anything to do with him; and then, again, in another way, it has. I want you to know that a blunder means something to a dispatcher besides the loss of his job. Do you think they're a cold-blooded, calloused lot? I want you to know that they care. Oh, yes, they're human. They've got a heart and they've got a soul; the one to break, the other to sear.

I said they didn't know much about Breen out here, except that he was a pretty good dispatcher; but as far as that goes it didn't help him any—rather the reverse, when the smash came. The better the man, the harder the fall—what? It's generally that way, isn't it?

Perhaps you're wondering what I know about him. I'll tell you. If anyone knew Breen, I knew him. I was only a kid then; I'm a man now. I hadn't even a coat—Breen gave me one. I'm a dispatcher—Breen taught me, and no better man on the "key" than Breen ever lived—a better man than I could ever hope to be—yet he slipped.

You probably read of the Elktail wreck at the time it happened, but you've forgotten about it by now. Those things don't live long in the mind unless they come pretty close home to you; there's too many other things happening every hour in this big, pulsing world to make it anything more than the sensation of the moment. But out here the details have cause enough to be fixed in the minds of most of us, not only of the wreck itself, but of what happened afterward, as well—and I don't know which of the two was the worse. You can judge for yourself.

I'm not going into technicalities. You'll understand better if I don't. You'll remember I said that the Hill Division is only single-tracked. That means, I don't need to tell you, that it's up to the dispatcher every second, and all that stands between the trains and eternity is the bit of tissue tucked in the engineer's blouse and its duplicate crammed in the conductor's side pocket. Orders, meeting points, single track, you understand? The dispatcher holds them all, every last one of them, for life or death—men, women and children, train crews, and company property, all—and Breen slipped!

No one to this day knows how it happened. I dare say some eminent authority on psychology might explain it, but the explanation would be too high-browed and too far over my head to understand it, even if he did. I only know the facts and the result.

Breen sent out a lap order on No. 1, the Imperial Limited, westbound, and No. 82, a fast freight, perishable, streaking east. Both were off schedule, and he was nursing them along for every second he could squeeze. Back through the mountains, both ways, all through the night, he'd given them the best of everything—the Imperial clear rights, and No. 82 pretty nearly, if not quite, as good. Then he fixed the meeting point for the two trains.

I read a story once where the dispatcher sent out a lap order on two trains, and his mistake was staring at him all the time from his order book. I guess that was a slip of the pen, and he never noticed it. That was queer enough, but what Breen did was queerer still.

His order book showed straight as a string. The freight was to hold at Muddy Lake, ten miles west of Elktail, for No. 1. No. 1, of course, as I told you, was running free. Somehow Breen wired the word "Elktail" instead of "Muddy Lake"—and never knew it—never had a hint that anything was wrong—never caught it on the repeat, and gave back his OK. The order, the written order in the book, was exactly as it should be. It read Muddy Lake—that was right. Muddy Lake. You see what happened? There wasn't time for the freight to make Elktail, but she got within three miles of it—and that's as far as she ever got! In a nasty piece of track, full of trestles and gorges, where the right of way bends worse than the letter S, they met, the two of them, head on—No. 1 and No. 82.

And Breen didn't know what he had done, even after the details began to pour in. How could he know? What was 82 doing east of Muddy Lake? She should have been waiting there for No. 1 to pass her. The order book showed that plain enough. And all through the rest of that night, while he worked like a madman clearing the line, getting up hospital, relief, and wrecking trains—with Carleton, who was super then, gray-faced and haggard, like the master of a storm-tossed liner on his bridge giving orders, pacing the room, cursing at times at his own impotency—Breen didn't know, neither of them knew, where the blame lay.

But the horror of the thing had Breen in its grip even then. I was there that night, and I can see him now bent over under the

"...and Breen slipped!" A head-on collision, circa 1912.

green-shaded lamp. I can see Carleton with that bulldog face of his, and it wasn't a pleasant face to see.

One thing I remember Breen said. Once, as the sounder pitilessly clicked a message more ghastly than any that had gone before, adding to the number of those whose lives had gone out forever, adding to the tale of the wounded, to the wild, mad, story of chaos and ruin, Breen lifted his head from the key for a moment, pushed his hair out of his eyes with a nervous, shaky sweep of his hand, and looked at Carleton.

"It's horrible, horrible," he whispered, "but think of the man who did it! Death would be easy compared to what he must feel. It makes me as weak as a kitten to think of it, Carleton. Man, don't you see! I, or any other dispatcher, might do this same thing tomorrow, the next day, or the day after. Tell me again, Carleton, tell me again, that order's straight?"

"Don't lose your nerve," Carleton answered sharply. "Whoever has blundered, it's not you."

Irony? No. It's beyond all that, isn't it? It's getting about as near to the tragedy of a man's life as you can get. It's getting as deep and tapping as near bedrock as we'll ever do this side of the Great Divide. Think of it! Think of Breen that night—it's too big to get, isn't it?

Those words of his have rung in my ears all these years, and that scene I can see over again in every detail every time I close my eyes.

In the few hours left before dawn that morning there wasn't time to give much attention to the cause. There was enough else to think of, enough to give every last man on the division all they could handle—the investigation could come later. But it never came. There was no need for one. How did they find out? It came like the crack of doom, and Breen got it—got it—and it seemed to burst the flood gates of his memory open, seemed to touch that dormant chord, and he knew, knew as he knew that he had a God, what he had done.

They found the order that made the meeting point Elktail tucked in Mooney's jumper when, after they got the crane at work, they hauled him out from under his engine. Who was Mooney? Engineer of the freight. They found him before they did any of his train crew, or his fireman, either, for that matter. Dead? Yes. I'm a dispatcher; look at it from the other side if you want to, it's only fair. That bit of tissue cleared Mooney, of course—but it sent him to his death. Yes, I know, don't you think I know what it means—to slip?

It was just before Davis, Breen's relief, came on for the morning trick—in fact, Davis was in the room when Breen got the report. He scribbled it on a pad, word for word, as it came in, for Carleton to see. For a minute it didn't seem to mean anything to him, and then, as I say, he got it. I never saw such a look on a man's face before, and I hope I never may again.

He seemed to wither up, blasted as the oak is blasted by a lightning stroke. The despair, the agony of his eyes are beyond any words of mine to describe, and you wouldn't want to hear it if I could tell you. He held out his arms pitifully like a pleading child. His lips moved, but he had to try over and over again before any sound came from them.

There was no thought of throwing the blame on anybody else. Breen wasn't that kind. Oh, yes, he could have done it. He could have put the blunder on the night man at The Gap, where Mooney received his Elktail holding order, and Breen's order book would have left it an open question as to which of the two had made the mistake—would probably have let him out and damned the other.

You say from the way he acted he didn't think of that, and therefore the temptation didn't come to him. Yes, I know what you mean. Not so much to Breen's credit—what? Well, I don't know; it depends on the way you look at it. I'd rather believe the thought didn't come, because the man's soul was too clean. It was clean then—no matter what he did afterward.

There have been death scenes of dispatchers before, many of them—there will be others in the days to come, many of them. So long as there are railroads, and so long as men are frail as men, lacking the infallibility of a higher power, just so long will they be inevitable. But no death scene of a dispatcher's career was ever as this one was. Breen was his own judge, his own jury, his own executioner. Do you think I could ever forget his words?

He pointed his hand toward the window that faced the western stretch of track, toward the foothills, toward the mighty peaks of the Rockies that towered beyond them, and the life, the being of the man was in his voice. They came slowly, those words, wrenched from a broken heart, torn from a shuddering soul:

"I wish to God that it was me in their stead. I did it, Carleton. I don't know how. I did it."

No one answered him. No one spoke. For a moment, that seemed like all eternity, there was silence, then Breen, his arms still held out before him, walked across the room as a blind man walks in his own utter darkness, walked to the door and passed out—alone. Those few steps across the room—alone! I've thought of that pretty often since—they seemed so significantly in keeping with what there was of life left for the stricken man—alone.

I don't know how I let him go like that. I was too stunned to move, I guess, but I reached him at the foot of the stairs as he stepped out onto the platform. There wasn't anything I could say, was there? What would you have said?

No man knew better than Breen himself what this would mean to him. He was wrecked, wrecked worse than that other wreck, for his was a living death. There weren't any grand juries or things of that kind out here; not that it would have made any difference to Breen if there had been. You can't put any more water in a pail when it's already full, can you? You can't add to the maximum, can you?

Don't you think Breen's punishment was beyond the reach of man or men to add to, or, for that matter, to abate by so much as the smallest fraction? It was—all except one final twinge, that I believe now settled him, though I'll say here that whatever it did to Breen it's not for me to judge her. Who am I that I should? It is between her and her Maker. I'll come to that in a minute.

Yes, Breen knew well enough what it meant to him, but his thoughts that morning as we walked up the street weren't, I know right well, on himself—he was thinking of those others. And I, well, I was thinking of Breen. Wouldn't you? I owed Breen everything I had in the world.

Neither of us said a word all the way up to his boarding house. It was almost as though I wasn't with him for all the attention he paid to me. But he knew I was there just the same. I like to think of that.

I wasn't very old then—I'm not offering that as an excuse, for I'm not ashamed to admit that I was near to tears—if I'd been older, perhaps I could have said or done something to help. As it was, all I could do was to turn that one black thought over and over and over again in my mind. Breen's living death, death, death, death.

That's the way it hit me, the way it caught me, and the word clung and repeated itself as I kept step beside him.

He was dead, dead to hope, ambition, future, everything, as dead as though he lay outstretched before me in his coffin. It seemed as if I could see him that way. And then, don't ask me why, I don't know; I only know such things happen, come upon you unconsciously, suddenly, there flashed into my mind that bit of verse from the Bible; you know it—"If a man die, shall he live again?"

I must have said it out loud without knowing it, for he whirled upon me quick as lightning, placed his two hands upon my shoulders, and stared with a startled gaze into my eyes. I say startled. It was, but there was more. There seemed for a second a gleam of hope awakened, hungry—oh, how hungry—pitiful in its yearning, and then the uselessness, the futility of that hope crushed it back, stamped it out, and the light in his eyes grew dull and died away.

We had halted at the door of his boarding house, and I made as though to go upstairs with him to his room, but he stopped me.

"Not now, Charlie boy," he said, shaking his head and trying to smile, "not now. I want to be alone."

And so I left him.

Maybe you'll think it queer that I left Breen like that, let him go to his room alone. You're thinking that in his condition he might do himself harm—end it all, to put it bluntly. Well, that thought didn't come to me then; it did afterward, but not then. Why? It must have been just the innate consciousness that he wouldn't do that sort of thing.

He was too big a man, big enough to have faced what was before him, faced the conditions, faced even the men, if it had not been for her. I want to stand right on this. Breen would never have done what he did if she had acted differently. That much I know. But, I want to say it again, I've no right to judge her.

Perhaps you've read that story of Kipling's about the Black Tyrone Regiment that saw their dead? Well, Breen, as I told you at the beginning, wasn't popular, and the boys had seen their dead. Do you understand? Pariah, outcast, what you like, they made him; all except pity they gave him; and I say he would have taken it all, accepted it all, only there are some things too heavy for a man to bear, aren't there? "Load limit," the engineers call it when they build their bridge. Well, there's a load limit on the heart and brain, and soul of a man just as there is on a bridge.

Kitty Mooney had seen her dead. Kitty Mooney, the engineer's sister! And Breen loved her, was going to marry her. That's all.

How do I know? How do you know? Perhaps it was grief; perhaps it was hysteria; perhaps it was according to the light God gave her, and she couldn't understand; perhaps it was only wild, unreasoning, frantic passion. I don't know. I only know she called him—a murderer.

She couldn't have loved him, you say. Perhaps no, perhaps yes. Does it make any difference? Breen thought she did, and Breen loved her. I don't know. I only know that where he looked for a ray of mercy, her mercy, to light the blackened depths, he received, instead, a condemnation more terrible than any that had gone before, and a bleeding heart dried bitter as gall, a patient, grief-stricken man became a vicious, snapping wolf, and "Angel" Breen—a devil.

It was pretty lawless out here in those days. We had the riffraff of the East, and worse; and there was nothing to restrain them, nothing much to keep them in check, and they did about as they liked. They brought the touch into the picture of the West that the West hasn't lived down yet, and I'm not sure ever will. The brawling, gambling, gun-handling type; the thief, the desperado, the bad man, rotten bad, bad to the core. They've been stamped out now, most of them, but it was different then. They didn't turn a cold shoulder to Breen. Why should they? They were outcasts and pariahs, too, weren't they? And Breen, well, I guess you understand as well as I do, and you know as I know that when a man like that goes, he goes the limit. There's no middle course for some men; they're not made that way.

Breen disappeared from Big Cloud, and I didn't see him from the day Kitty Mooney turned him from her door until the night—but I'm coming to that—that's the end. There's a word or two that goes before—so that you'll understand. He disappeared from Big Cloud, but he didn't leave the mountains. Maybe back of it all—an almost impossible theory, if you like, but I can understand it—a something in him wouldn't let him run away.

He did run away, you say? Yes, but there's the queer brain kink again. Perhaps he temporized. You temporize. I temporize. We try to fool and delude sometimes, snatch at loopholes, snatch at straws, to bolster up our self-respect, don't we? That's what I mean when I say it's possible he couldn't run away. He clung to the straw, the loophole, that running away was measured in miles. I don't say that was it, for I don't know. It's possible. We heard of him from time to time as the months went by, and the things we heard weren't pleasant things to hear. He drifted from bad to worse, until that something that he couldn't do brought him to a halt—brought the end.

Don't ask me when Breen threw in his lot with Black Dempsey and the band of fiends that called him leader—the ugliest, soul-blackened set of fiends that ever polluted the West, and that's using pretty strong language. Don't ask me how Breen got to Big Cloud that night away from the others waiting to begin their brutal work. Don't ask me. I don't know. Why he did it—is different. That I can tell you. What they wanted him to do, to have a part in, was that one thing I was speaking about, the one thing he couldn't do.

Breen was a railroad man, railroading was in his blood, that's all—but it's everything—railroading was in his blood. As for the rest, maybe he didn't know what they were up to until the last moment, and then stole away from them. Maybe they found it out, suspected him, and some of them followed him, tried to stop him, tried to keep him from reaching here. But what's the use of speculating? I never knew. I never will know. Breen can't tell me, can he? And all that I can tell you is what I saw that night.

I had the night trick then—Breen's job—they gave me Breen's job. It seemed somehow at first like sacrilege to take it—as though I was robbing him of it, taking it away from him, wronging, stripping, impoverishing the man to whom I owed even the knowledge that made me fit, that made it possible, to hold down a key—his key.

Of course, that was only sensitiveness, but you understand, don't you? It caught me hard when I first "sat in," but gradually the feeling wore off, not that I ever forgot; I haven't yet, for that matter; only time blunts the sharp edges, and routine, habit, and custom do the rest. I don't need to tell you that I remember that night. Remember it! That was before this station was built, and in those days we had an old wooden shack here that did duty for freight house, station, division headquarters, and everything else all rolled into one. The dispatcher's room was upstairs.

Things were moving slick as a whistle that night. No extra traffic, no road troubles, in—out, in—out, all along the line, from one end of the division to the other, the trains were running like clockwork. If there was anything on my mind at all, it was the Limited, No. 2, eastbound. We were handling a good deal of gold in those days; there was a lot of it being shipped East then—is still, from the Klondyke now, you know—and we were getting a fair share of the business away from the southern competition.

We hadn't had any trouble, weren't looking for any, but it was pretty generally understood that all shipments of that kind were to get special attention.

No. 2 was carrying an extra express car with a consignment for the mint that night; so, naturally, I had kept my eye on her more closely than usual all the way through the mountains from the time I got her from the Western Division.

At the time I'm speaking about, four o'clock in the morning, I was almost clear of her, for she wasn't much west of Coyote Bend, fifteen miles from here, and she had rights all the way in. Half an hour more, at the most, and she would be off my hands and up to the dispatchers of the Prairie Division.

She had held her schedule to the tick every foot of the way, and all I was waiting for was the call from Coyote Bend that would report her in and out again into the clear for Big Cloud. Coyote Bend is the first station west of here, you understand? There's nothing between.

She was due at Coyote at 4:05, and I want you to remember this—I said it before, but I want to repeat it, I want you to get it hard—she had run to the second all through the night.

My watch was open on the table before me, and I watched the minute hand creep round the dial—4:03, 4:04, 4:05,—4:06— 4:07—4:08. I was alone in the office. The night caller had gone out perhaps ten minutes before to call the train crew of the 5 o'clock local. There wasn't anything to be nervous about; I don't put it down to that. Three minutes wasn't anything. You know how it is when you're waiting for something to happen, and I was expecting the sounder to break every second with that report from Coyote Bend.

Anyway—put it down to what you like—though I didn't want a drink particularly, I pushed back my chair, got up and walked over to the water cooler. The dispatcher's table was on the east side of the room, the door opened on the south side, and the water cooler was over in the opposite corner. I'm explaining this so that you'll understand that the door was between the water cooler and the table.

That old shack was rough and ready, and I've wondered more than once what kept it from falling to pieces. It didn't take more than a breath of wind to set every window sash in the outfit rattling like a corps of snare drums.

That's why, I guess, I didn't hear anyone coming up the stairs. It was blowing pretty hard that night. But I heard the door open. I thought it was the caller back again, and I wondered how he'd made his rounds in such quick time. With the tumbler half up to my lips I turned around—then the glass slipped from my fingers and crashed into slivers on the floor. My mouth went dry, my heart seemed to stop. I couldn't speak, couldn't move. It was Breen—"Angel" Breen!

I saw him start at the noise of the splintering glass, but he didn't look at me. He clung swaying to the door jamb for an instant, his face chalky white, then he reeled across the room and dropped into his old chair. I saw him glance at my watch and his face seemed to go whiter than before.

Then he snatched at the train sheet, and a smile—no, it wasn't exactly a smile; you couldn't call it that, his whole face seemed to change, light up, and his lips moved, I know now in a prayer of gratitude. You understand, don't you? He knew the time card, knew that No. 2, after he had seen my watch, should have been out of Coyote Bend four, perhaps five, minutes before, but the train sheet showed her still unreported.

His fingers closed on the key and he began to make the Coyote Bend call. Over and over, quick, sharp, clear, incisive, with all the old masterful touch of his sending Breen was rattling the call— "CX"—"CX"—"CX"—"CX!"

And then I found my voice.

"Breen!" I stammered, and started toward him. "You! What—"

The sounder broke. Coyote Bend answered. And on the instant Breen flashed this order over the wire:

"Hold No. 2! Hold No. 2"—twice the sender spelled out the words.

Then Coyote Bend repeated the order, and Breen gave back the OK.

"Breen!" I shouted. "What are you doing? Are you crazy? What are you doing here? Speak, man, what—"

He had straightened in his chair, and a sort of low, catchy gasp came from his lips. It seemed as though it took all his power, all his strength, to lift his eyes to mine. I sprang for the key, but he jerked himself suddenly forward and pushed me desperately away. And then he called me by the old name, not much above a whisper, I could hardly catch the words, and I didn't understand, didn't know, that the man before me was a wounded, dying man. My brain was whirling, full of that other night, full of the days and months that had followed. I couldn't think. I—

"Charlie—boy, it's all right. Black Dempsey in the cut. I was afraid I was too late—too late. They shot me—here," he was tearing with his fingers at his waistcoat.

And then I understood, too late. As I reached for him he swayed forward and toppled, a huddled heap, over the key, over the order book, over the train sheet that once had taken his life and now had given it back to him—dead.

What is there to say? Whatever he may have done, however far he may have fallen, back of it all, through it all, bigger than himself, stronger than any other bond, was the railroading that was in his blood. Breen was a railroad man.

I don't know why, do I? You don't know why, after No. 2 had run to schedule all that night, it happened just when it did. It might have happened at some other time, but it didn't. Luck or chance, if you like, more than that if you'd rather think of it in another way, but just a few miles west of Coyote Bend something went wrong in the cab of No. 2.

Nothing much; I don't remember now what it was, don't know that I ever knew; nothing much. Just enough to hold her back a few minutes, the few minutes that let Breen sit in again on the night dispatcher's trick, sit in again at the key, hold down his old job once more before he quit railroading forever with the order that he gave his life to send, to keep No. 2 from rushing to death and destruction against the rocks and boulders Black Dempsey and his gang had piled across the track in the cut five miles east of Coyote Bend.

I don't know. "If a man die, shall he live again?" I leave it to you. I only know that they think a lot of him out here, think a lot of Breen, "Angel" Breen now.

Frank L. Packard, "The Night Dispatcher," *The Railway Conductor* 29, no. 8 (August 1912): 570-78.

THE HOLDUP OF NO. 8

Theatrical flyer from 1896.

Train robberies were so common in the late nineteenth century that some railroads issued firearms to their trainmen. After all, it was relatively easy to stop a train: either force a depot operator to put up a stop signal, or swing a red signal lantern across the track, a signal that no engineer dared ignore.

Freight trains were generally unmolested by robbers. It was the passenger trains they wanted. In addition to the money and jewelry that the passengers carried, most passenger trains contained an express car in its consist—the Victorian version of overnight or short-time delivery service. The express car nearly always contained money, for there was no electronic transfer of funds in those days. If a payroll were to be met, or a large payment to be made, it usually went by express.

And so any small depot in the middle of nowhere became the possible location of a robbery, sooner or later. If well executed, *most holdups were successful. But every once in a while, even the best-planned robberies met with an unpleasant surprise, such as **The Holdup of No. 8.***

I n the early part of the 80's I was holding down a sidetrack OS job on the main line of the U.P. in western Wyoming. There was a depot, section house, and water tank at the place, the nearest neighbors being at the next station, sixteen miles away. I was fresh from the East; and the lonely nights I spent in that out-of-the-way place, listening to the doleful wail of the coyotes and occasional screams of mountain lions, were indeed nerve-racking.

I had bought a Winchester and a Colt's six-shooter, and took great pride in "packing" it by means of a scabbard and belt, with the belt bristling with cartridges, strapped loosely around my waist. The outfit presented a very formidable appearance, and was the cause of many sly winks, nodding of heads, and indulgent jests on the part of the trainmen. While I presumed it had the opposite effect, my make-up proclaimed the "tenderfoot" with emphasis.

One night, while a crew was in the office getting orders and waiting for a stock train, a brakeman, who, by the way, was a jolly good fellow, spoke, as I took it, casually to the boys about an operator who had been killed by train robbers several years before at that very place. The conversation became general, and the boys entered into the scheme with energy.

They told, with horrible detail, how the unfortunate operator was surprised at the very table where I was sitting, by a gang of train robbers, and ordered to stop No. 8, the *Overland Through Express,* due at my station shortly after midnight, and that the operator refused and showed fight, and was instantly shot and killed by the outlaws. I did not observe the sly winks exchanged between the crew, and was very much disturbed by the story of the tragedy.

Ely Saunders, the engineer, asked me what I would do if train robbers tried to hold me up some night. I pointed significantly at my six-shooter and Winchester and replied that I should make it hot for the outfit that tried it. This was the occasion for a general burst of good-natured laughter that I never did understand until a great while later.

The stock train showed up and the boys bade me goodnight, cheerily warning me to be careful if train robbers or Indians should attack me, and I was left alone with the unpleasant reflections of the tragic end of my predecessor several degrees removed.

The *Overland Express*, No. 8, was due at 2:17 in the morning, and I had until that time to take a few hours' nap on the table. I lay down and tried to sleep, but couldn't. About 1:30, my fire being low, I went across the track to the coal house after coal. I opened the coal house door, picked up the shovel, and was just in the act of shoving it into the coal pile when a rough voice from behind commanded, "Hands up there, young fellar!" I whirled around only to confront a masked individual and the muzzle of a six-shooter stuck in my face; at the same moment another masked man deliberately stepped up and pulled my valued six-shooter out of its scabbard and put it in his pocket with a chuckle of satisfaction.

The only means of escape seemed for me to crawl into the barrel of that gun, and it certainly looked large enough. Five masked men— train robbers—stood around me. I was face to face with reality.

"Wall, young fellar," drawled the leader, "you jist march into the house now, do what we tell yer, and no monkey business, and you may get out of this with a whole skin; and if yer don't, I reckon we'll have to pepper yer full o' holes, for we ain't goin' to be balked by a tenderfoot fresh from the East, not if we know who's who, and I reckon we do."

I felt like one in a terrible nightmare. A chill forty degrees below zero ran trembling up my spinal column, down my arms, and oozed off of my fingertips. I could not have spoken a word if my life had depended upon it. I started with trembling steps toward the office door. One ruffian took me by the collar and shoved me right along into the office and plumped me down in my chair.

"Now, young fellar," demanded the leader, "you just turn that red light; then I guess we'll have to tie yer down—yer might monkey with them tickers thar and spile our plans."

I found my voice, and tremulously protested against being tied. But one of the party, with a harsh voice and wicked eyes, told me to shut up, and not make a damned fool of myself, in language that could not be misunderstood.

They pulled my chair back in one corner of the office, tied me in it, and sat down to await the coming of the train. They talked over the plans of their attack freely, paying no attention to me. They were to wait until the conductor and engineer came in to sign their orders, hold them up, take charge of the train, rob it, and get away. One they called "Tex" was to jump on the engine and "nail" the fireman. The balance were to attack the express car and rob the passengers, leaving one they called "Griff," who had my new six-shooter, to guard the trainmen when they got them into the office.

How proudly the robber fingered my new six-shooter! They had also appropriated my new Winchester, and my belt of cartridges the leader had buckled around him without a word of comment or even thanks to me.

No. 8 was right on time, whistled for the station, answered the red signal, dashed up to the office, and stopped.

The unsuspecting conductor, engineer, and brakeman ran into the office for their orders—and they got them. What a difference came over those robbers from when they were dealing with me. This was actual business.

"Hands up!" roared the leader, and four pairs of six-shooters covered the crew. The conductor and engineer instantly obeyed. The brakeman, a nervous little fellow, wheeled around, screamed, "My God, I'm killed!" and bolted out of the door and down the platform, yelling "robbers" at the top of his voice. Griff blazed away at him with my new six-shooter as he went out of the door.

"To your work, men!" shouted the leader, and three of the robbers started for the express car, the fourth commanding the conductor and engineer to line up against the wall, keep their hands up and their mouths shut. The robbers fired a few shots along the cars and proceeded to rob the train. I wondered if they would come in and shoot me in their excitement, and feared that they would. I could hear women screaming in the train, and men demanding in excited voices what was the matter.

From the rear of the train revolvers began to crack. Few at first, then like a bunch of lighted firecrackers, only on a larger scale. The shooting came nearer and the robber guarding the crew made a move as if to shoot the engineer, but the conductor said: "My God, man, don't shoot us; we are defenseless."

At that instant the door burst open, a blinding flash, a deafening report, and Mr. Griff plunged forward with a bullet in his head, before he had time to raise a hand. An officer, wearing the fatigue uniform of a captain in the United States Army, rushed into the room, followed by several soldiers.

The firing had ceased. A detachment of United States Cavalry was on the train en route from one of the western forts to another.

Swift and certain justice. Dead train robbers, Sanderson, Texas, 1912.

I was cut loose, and the first thing I did was to step timidly forward to where the dead robber lay, gather up my treasured six-shooter, and hand it to the captain, informing him that it was mine, and that I gave it to him.

"Don't want it," he replied in a kind but very firm voice. I placed the gun in the table drawer, and went out with the soldiers, conductor, and engineer to see how matters stood.

The soldiers were gathered in groups around the prostrate forms of the dead robbers. Four of them were dead, including the leader. The fifth had jumped from the engine when the firing began and made his escape.

That outfit of robbers had missed their calculation. They had not figured on a carload of soldiers being on the train with their sidearms. They loaded the bodies of the dead bandits into the express car and pulled out, leaving me alone at the station.

I "OS'd" No. 8 with trembling hand, told the dispatcher what had happened, sent in my resignation, and asked for a pass back East.

F.R. Dresbach, "The Holdup of No. 8," *The Railroad Trainman* 35, no. 4 (April 1918): 259-60.

A Glossary of Railroad Words and Terms Found in This Anthology

NOTE: The definitions listed below represent the meaning of the word or phrase as it was understood in the context of the stories in this collection. In some cases those meanings have changed with time.

ADJUSTING THE WIRES—Resetting the sensitivity of a telegraph due to variations in line voltage.

AGENT—The principal representative of the railroad at a station. Agents performed many of the same functions as an operator, including telegraphic communications.

ANGLE COCK—A valve used to open or close the air brake line. The angle cock was located at each end of a car, alongside the coupler.

ANNUL AN ORDER—To cancel a previously issued train order.

ANSWER A FLAG—To acknowledge a hand, light, or flag signal to stop, usually with a whistle blast from the engine.

APPLYING THE AIR—Setting the airbrakes throughout the length of the train from a brake lever in the cab.

BALLAST—The roadbed upon which the track and ties sat. Ballast could consist of crushed stone, cinders, or dirt. The ballast drained water away from the track, thus helping to prevent warping or sagging of the track.

BALLOON STACK—A large, flared smokestack on an engine. Balloon stacks were usually found on wood-burning engines. The balloon stack contained baffle plates to inhibit the discharge of large embers, which posed a fire hazard to wooden trestles and other structures, not to mention any bordering forest.

BINDLE STIFF—A hobo, especially one who carried a bedroll or bundle (bindle). The bindle usually was tied on the end of a pole that the hobo slung over his shoulder.

BLOWER—A device on the engine designed to increase the draft of air through the firebox, thereby creating more steam in the boiler.

BLOWING OFF STEAM—When the steam pressure within the boiler exceeded the limit of the safety valve, the valve would open and a heavy rush of steam automatically would escape into the air.

BOILER HEAD—The rear portion of the boiler, which included the opening into the firebox. The engine gauges, valves, and throttle were hung from the boiler head. Also referred to as the "backhead."

BOILER TUBE—See "flue."

BOOMER—A seasonal or temporary railroad employee who traveled from place to place for employment.

BRAKE BEAM—A steel-clad wooden crossbeam that pressed the brake shoes against the wheel surface.

BRAKE CLUB—A short, stout wooden baton used to gain leverage when turning a brake wheel.

BRAKEMAN—A crewmember—usually there were two on a train crew—who coupled and uncoupled the cars, aligned switches, and set the brakes by hand when necessary. Slang terms for a brakeman included brakie, shack, and car-grabber. One brakeman usually rode on the engine, the other in the caboose.

BRAKE WHEEL—A heavy, iron spindle, located at one end of a car, used to manually set the brakes.

BROWNIES—Brownie points, or demerits. The term was derived from a system of rewards and demerits devised by George R. Brown, a railroad executive, in 1886.

BUFFER PLATES—Similar to bumpers (see), buffers were metal plates on the ends of passenger car platforms that absorbed shock caused by slack run-in.

BUMPER—A protruding beam or metal plate on the end of some cars that relieved pressure on the couplers during a sudden braking or hard coupling. The term also was applied to the coupler housing.

BUNCH THE SLACK—All car couplers were inherently loose—enough so as to allow several feet of slack to develop over the length of a train. Bunching the slack—also known as running in the slack or taking up slack—meant forcing the cars closer together. This could be accomplished by braking a moving train and thus taking advantage of momentum to push the rear cars forward, or by backing up the engine against a stopped train.

CABOOSE—Also known as a waycar, van, crummy, or hack, the caboose was the traveling office for the conductor and a vantage point for the brakeman to watch over the train. Besides the conductor's desk and the cupola, the caboose usually contained bunks, an equipment locker, a heating or cooking stove, and a commode. The caboose normally was coupled at the rear of a freight train.

CALL-BOOK—A sign-in register indicating that a trainman was present for duty.

CALLBOY—A railroad employee whose job it was to locate and notify off-duty train crewmen for a coming shift. Sometimes referred to as a "caller."

CAR-GRABBER—A brakeman.

C&E—The term used on train orders to address the conductor and engineer.

CINDER—The fused ash remnant of burnt coal.

CLINKER—An unburnable piece of coal, usually the result of impurities.

CLOSE THE KEY—Disconnect from the telegraph circuit; essentially, to hang up.

COMPOUND—A locomotive with two sets of cylinders on each side.

CONDUCTOR—The crewman in charge of the train. Also called the con, captain, or cap.

CONSOLIDATION—A steam engine that featured two small pilot wheels and eight coupled driving wheels. The consolidation normally was used for freight service.

COPY 3—Make three copies of a train order. One would go to the engineer, one to the conductor, and one for the station files.

COUPLER—The mechanical locking device that held two cars together. The automatic coupler used by the turn of the century, also known as the Janney coupler, resembled the shape and bending motion of the human hand and fingers. See also "link and pin."

COWCATCHER—An attachment located on the front of most engines that was meant to knock any large obstruction from the track. The typical cowcatcher of the period was slanted downward and outward from an angled center ridge.

COUPLING LINK—See "link and pin."

CROWN SHEET—The top, inner portion of the firebox.

CUTTING OFF—Setting the lever (see) to limit the amount of steam entering the cylinder with each piston stroke. Cutting off would save steam and thus increase the boiler pressure.

CYLINDER—The cylindrical-shaped housing located on either side of the engine, in front of the drivers, that contained the piston. It was in the cylinder that steam pressure was converted to motion.

DAY-COACH—A chair car; a passenger car with seats that did not convert to berths for sleeping.

DIAL—The steam pressure gauge.

DIAMONDS—Coal from the tender.

DISPATCHER—A mid-level employee who orchestrated the movement of trains over a division, via telegraphic or telephonic communication with his agents and operators. The dispatcher's job can best be compared to the modern-day air traffic controller.

DISTANT (SIGNAL)—A trackside signal set in advance of the entrance to the territory that it was intended to protect. A distant signal was placed where a curve or other obstruction might have prevented the engineer from seeing the home signal (see) in time to react. The distant signal displayed the same indication as the home signal.

DIVISION—A geographic area under the control of a dispatcher and a superintendent. The length of a division varied according to traffic and density.

DOME—A reference to the steam dome, which was located on top of the boiler. High-pressure steam from the boiler collected in the dome, where the throttle opening was located. The steam dome was further covered with an outer casing.

DOUBLE THE ROAD (OR HILL)—Usually a hill, as series of hills, or a long grade was "doubled" when the engine could not pull the entire train up the grade due to tonnage or steepness. In that case the engine would take approximately half the train up the hill, leave it parked on a parallel track, run back down to the second half of the train, and pull it up the same hill.

DOUBLEHEADER—Two engines assigned to pull a train.

DOWN BRAKES—A term meaning "set the brakes." An engineer could signal for down brakes with one short blast of the whistle.

DOWN IN THE CORNER—Setting the lever (see) in the forward-most notch. This setting allowed steam to enter the cylinders for the full stroke of the piston, which created more power but also consumed more steam.

DRAG—A line of (usually) heavy freight cars. The term was also applied to a slow, heavy freight train.

DRAWBAR—The stem, or shank, that holds the coupler in place. The term has been used interchangeably, though incorrectly, with "drawhead."

DRAWHEAD—A coupler; specifically the face, or non-moving portion, of the coupler.

DRIVERS—The large, powered wheels of a steam locomotive, located directly below the boiler. The drivers, or driving wheels, as they sometimes were called, carried most of the locomotive's weight and were fixed to one another on each side by a rod—the side rod. One set of drivers was additionally connected to the main rod (see).

DRIVER SHOES—The brake shoes that press against the driving wheels of an engine.

DWARF SWITCH—A low switch stand and lever used for changing the direction of a turnout.

EAGLE EYE—Slang for a locomotive engineer.

EIGHT WHEELER—Another name for a mogul engine (see).

EXPRESS CAR—Usually part of a passenger or mail train, the express car carried packages and, quite often, cash or gold. Several express companies had contracts with various railroads to ship such expedited freight, and the express cars themselves often carried an "express messenger"—an employee of the express company—to handle the forwarding and to look after the security of the shipments. In appearances, express cars looked much like baggage cars.

EXTRA (TRAIN)—A train that was not listed on the schedule, or a scheduled train that was more than twelve hours late.

EXTRA BOARD—A seniority list of crewmen who were otherwise unassigned to a regular run.

FACING POINT SWITCH—A turnout in which the diverging rails face the approaching train or car.

FIFTEEN BY TWENTY-TWO—The size, in inches, of the cylinder diameter and the piston stroke, respectively.

FIFTY PERCENT AIR—When the Railroad Safety Appliance Act was passed by Congress in 1893, it required, amongst other things, that railroad engineers be able to stop their trains from the cab. The law went into effect in 1900 and was interpreted as meaning that at least half of the cars of a freight train be equipped with air brakes, hence "fifty percent air."

FIRE-BOY—Slang for fireman, the engine crewman who stoked the boiler fire and kept watch on the boiler water level. See also "tallow bucket."

FIREBOX—A large, grated area under the rear of the boiler in which fuel was burned. The heat from the firebox transferred through the overhead crown sheet into the boiler water, thus creating steam.

FIRE DOOR—The heavy, steel door that opened into the firebox under the boiler head. The fire doors varied in size, but were always large enough to allow the fireman to throw in a scoop of coal.

FLAG BOTH WAYS—To place a flagman (see) in front of and behind a stopped train.

FLAGMAN—A crewmember whose job was to protect a stopped train. The flagman positioned himself several hundred yards in front of or in rear of his train with a red flag, lantern, and torpedoes, in order to warn any approaching train. Oftentimes the fireman served as the head-end flagman.

FLANGER—A wing-bladed device used to remove snow, or sometimes ballast, from between the rails.

FLIMSY—Common term for the tissue-thin paper on which train orders were written.

FLUE—Internal dry pipes that carried hot gasses from the firebox through the boiler. The greater number of flues meant a greater transfer of heat to the boiler water.

FROG—See "switch frog."

FULL PIT—A reference to the forward part of the coal bin on an engine tender.

FUSEE—A flare.

GANGWAY—The passageway between the cab and the tender.

GAY-CATS—Inexperienced hoboes.

GLIM—A railroad lantern.

GOAT—A small engine used for shuttling various pieces of equipment and cars in a yard area.

GUARD RAILS—A second set of track rails that ran parallel to the through rails. Guard rails normally were spiked down inside the running rails to catch an errant wheel that might have derailed. Guard rails most often were found on bridges, tight curves, and close clearances along the main line.

GUNNELS—Longitudinal support rods that formed part of the underframe of freight and passenger cars. Also known as rods.

HACK—Slang term for a caboose.

HELPER (ENGINE)—A second, or even third, engine assigned to help with a heavy train over a grade. Helpers could be coupled on at the front end, the rear end, or mid-train, depending on the circumstances of the grade, the curves, and the total tonnage. Helper engines in steam days each required their own engineer and fireman.

HIGHBALL—1.) To move with all possible speed; 2.) A signal to begin a run.

HOBO—1.) A nomadic traveler who rode trains surreptitiously without a ticket or without permission; 2.) A railroad laborer, usually a member of a traveling track gang.

HOG—A steam locomotive.

HOGGER—A locomotive engineer.

HOME (SIGNAL)—A trackside signal placed at the starting point of the territory that it controlled. In some cases, the home signal was augmented with a distant signal (see) that displayed the same indication.

HOOK—A long rake-like iron rod used by the fireman to arrange the bed of burning coal within the firebox.

HOOKING UP—The term referred to pulling back on the lever (see) in order to shorten the cut-off time of steam entering into the cylinders.

Hooking up usually took place on a downgrade or on a flat grade, thus taking advantage of momentum to move the train.

HOSTLER—A yard employee whose primary job was to move engines to and from the roundhouse, coal chute, water tank, or other maintenance areas.

HOT BOX—An overheated axle bearing.

HOUSE TRACK—The side track near a station that served a freight house or freight platform.

I—Telegraphic shorthand that essentially meant: "I acknowledge your call."

INJECTOR—A steam-operated device on the engine that forced water into the boiler under pressure.

INTERLOCKING (PLANT)—A system of interconnected switches and signals arranged in such a manner that made it impossible to set a signal to display "clear" when a switch was in the wrong position. The controlling interlocking levers, usually located in a tower, were attached to an array of notched bars and magnetic catches that required a specific operating sequence. Once a route had been set and signaled, no intervening track switch could be thrown to interfere with the intended route.

JACKET—The outer casing of the boiler.

JOHNSON BAR—See "lever."

JOURNAL BOXES—The bearing and lubrication enclosures at the ends of each axle.

JULL PLOW—A snow plow that utilized a diagonally-mounted auger conveyor.

KEY—The portion of the telegraph apparatus that the operator manipulated by tapping to produce an open and closed electrical circuit. This, in turn, created the staccato clicking of Morse code.

LEAD TRACK—A primary yard track that opened into several parallel tracks. Also known as a drill track, the switch engine used the lead as a back-and-forth track to sort cars into their proper groupings.

LEVER—Also known as the Johnson bar or reverse lever, it was mounted vertically in front of or alongside the engineer's seat. The lever controlled the cut-off point of steam entering into the engine cylinders on any given stroke. Adjusting the position of the lever was known as "notching her up" (pulling the lever back), or "shoving her in the corner" (setting the lever at the full forward, maximum power position). Pulling the lever to a rearward position on the quadrant would place the engine in reverse.

LIFT THE PIN—To pull the pin that locks the coupler in the closed position; to uncouple.

LIGHT ENGINE—An engine traveling without any cars coupled to it.

LIMITED—A generic name given to fast passenger/express/mail trains whose schedule called for a limited number of stops between the end terminals of the run. Limiteds were likely to whiz through small towns, picking up and dropping off a mail bag on the fly.

LINK AND PIN—An archaic coupling device that consisted of a heavy, elongated link and a locking pin. The link was placed in a coupling box located on the end of a car and the pin was dropped through a hole in the box to hold the link in place. It was a dangerous method of coupling and was outlawed after 1900 for cars in interchange service.

LOCAL—A freight train that picked up and set out cars at sidings and industries over a relatively short distance, then returned to the point of origin. The term can also be applied to a passenger train that ran a short distance out and back, stopping at all stations along the way.

LOOKING OVER THE AIR—Checking the air brake connections from car to car.

MAIN ROD—The heavy working beam that connected the piston rod to the driving wheels. It was the main rod that converted the back-and-forth motion of the piston rod to the rotary motion of the drivers (see "drivers"). The main rods were located on either side of the engine—one for each piston.

MARKERS—Signal lanterns hung on the rear of a train.

MOGUL—A steam locomotive with two pilot wheels on the front, followed by six larger driving wheels. Moguls were common freight engines during the turn-of-the-century era and saw occasional duty on slower passenger trains.

MOTOR—A motor car; a self-propelled baggage-mail car and coach, powered by external electricity or by a gasoline-generator combination.

ON THE CARPET—To stand before the superintendent to answer for a breach of procedure.

OPERATOR—The telegraph operator at a depot. The operator transmitted and copied both railroad business and telegrams. The operator was junior in seniority to the station agent, who usually worked the day shift. The operator often was required to perform routine bookkeeping and record keeping tasks at the station when not engaged in telegraphic chores.

OPERATOR'S TISSUE—See "flimsy."

ORDER BOARD—A signal device at a station or tower used to inform the crew of an approaching train that they had an order awaiting them.

ORDERS—Written instructions to the train crew, usually sent from the dispatcher by telegraph.

OS—Telegraphic shorthand used to report to the dispatcher that a train had arrived or passed a station. The station operator would send the OS followed by the station call sign, the train number, and the time. A typical call would read: "OS DE. No. 92 by at 9:15."

PALACE CAR—A first-class sleeping car, decorated in the ornate tastes of the late Victorian era. See "sleeper."

PILOT—The front platform of a locomotive; or the front set of guiding wheels under the same.

PIT—A trench for dumping coal or wood ash from the firebox. The ash pit was placed between the rails on a service track.

PONY TRUCK—The two small guide wheels located at the front of an engine under the pilot.

POUND THE BRASS—Operate a telegraph key.

POWER-YARD—The engine service and storage area of a railroad yard.

PULLED HIS DOOR—Opened the firebox door.

PULLING A DRAWBAR—Breaking a coupler shank, usually the result of too much strain or jerky operation.

RAKING THE FIRE—Smoothing out the burning coal bed in the engine firebox so as to insure an equal distribution of heat.

REVERSE LEVER—See "lever."

RODS—See 1.) "gunnels"; or 2.) "drivers."

ROTARY SNOWPLOW—A large, steam-powered device that utilized a revolving blade mounted on a horizontal axis to remove snow from the tracks and throw it to one side. The rotary was pushed by one or more engines.

ROUNDHOUSE—An enclosed, semi-circular service facility for steam locomotives. Engines entered their assigned stall in the roundhouse via a revolving turntable, which also served to face the engine in the proper direction.

RUN-BOARD, or RUNNING BOARD—A narrow walkway that ran along the top of boxcars, and along the side frames of certain other types of cars, thus enabling trainmen to traverse the length of a moving train. Running boards were not installed on flatcars or gondolas, as the trainmen could climb over the car's cargo.

SAFETY VALVE—A device located on top of the locomotive that would release excess steam from the boiler. The release pressure could be adjusted by a tensioning spring. Also known as a "pop" or "relief valve."

SAND-BOX—A protruding bin on top of the engine boiler that held sand. The sand was piped down to the rail, in front of the drivers. The engineer could open the sand valve and thus dust the rails, which would provide better adhesion for the drivers.

SAWING (or SAWING BY)—A back and forth switching maneuver that was used when two trains were to pass one another, but when one or both trains were longer than the available passing siding.

SECTION (OF A TRAIN)—If the total tonnage of a train movement made it necessary to dispatch two or more trains on the same schedule (with a safety interval of several minutes between them), then each train would be dispatched as first, second, third, etc., section of a given train number. In the case of, say, train number 25, with two sections, those two trains would be called first No. 25 and second No. 25, and written as 1/25 and 2/25.

SECTION (OF TRACK)—A territory of perhaps ten or fifteen miles that was maintained by a track gang. The gang worked under the authority of a section foreman. There usually was a section house located approximately midway along the section where the track gang ate and slept.

SET-DOWN—An invitation to a hobo to sit down at a table for a meal. A set-down usually was offered by a sympathetic family or individual.

SET HIS AIR—An engineer applying the air brakes to the train.

SHOW RED—To display a red board, semaphore signal, or lantern at a station; the signal for an approaching train to stop. Showing red was the opposite of a white (later, green) signal, which indicated a clear track ahead.

SHUT OFF—Close the throttle, thereby slowing or stopping the train.

SIDE ROD—See "drivers."

SIDING—A side track. Some sidings were double-ended (i.e., attached by a switch to the main track at either end) and commonly were used for passing purposes. A stub siding diverted from the main track only at one end and often served a trackside industry.

SLACK—The inherent looseness of couplings, which increases dramatically with each additional car. Slack can "run in" when the train slows, or "run out" when the train accelerates.

SLEEPER, or SLEEPING CAR—A passenger car that could be converted from seats in the daytime to beds at night. The berths usually were set in two tiers, bunk style, with a partition between sections and heavy privacy drapes facing the aisle. Some sleeping cars featured staterooms or drawing rooms—semi-permanent spaces with bulkheads and doors.

SLOW ORDER—A directive from the dispatcher that all trains were to run at a reduced speed through a certain stretch of track. Slow orders usually were issued due to track maintenance, localized flooding, or other anomalies. The term, "put the orders on him," referred to an engineer thus directed to run slow.

SNOW SHED—A timbered roof built over the tracks to prevent the accumulation of snow. Snow sheds were common along mountain cuts.

SOUNDER—A component of a telegraph set, the sounder was the electromechanical device that emitted the clicking cadence sound of Morse code. The sounder usually was mounted on a small L-shaped wooden shelf that, in turn, was attached to a scissors-type extension arm. It was traditional, even necessary, to amplify the clicking sound by wedging a tin tobacco can between the sounder and back of the wooden shelf.

SPANNER—A wrench.

STATION REPORT—A routine report that listed, among other things, the status of cars set out or picked up.

STAY BOLT—A long-shanked spacer bolt that held the inner boiler to the outer shell.

SWITCH—A turnout; a geometric arrangement of track utilizing the lateral movement of rails in such a way that it allowed a train or car to divert (switch) from one track to an adjoining track. "Throwing a switch" meant aligning the direction of a turnout.

SWITCHBACK—A track arrangement utilized on very steep grades. A switchback was essentially a zig-zag configuration, whereby a train must move forward on one leg, then back through the next leg, all the while climbing or descending the grade.

SWITCHER—A locomotive designed for shuffling cars in a yard. Switchers were easy to spot because they did not have small pilot wheels on the front, as did road engines.

SWITCH FROG—The V-shaped portion of a turnout where the two inside rails diverge from one another.

'TABLE—See "turntable."

TAKE SIDING—Common term for a train to switch off the main track onto a siding and await the passage of another train.

TAKING WATER—Filling the water tank on an engine tender.

TALLOW BUCKET—A large can for carrying rendered animal fat. The tallow was used for lubricating moving parts on the engine. The tallow was kept warm and fluid by storing it on a shelf on the boiler backhead. Since the fireman sometimes was required to step out onto the moving engine and lubricate the rods, the name "tallow-pot" was used as yet another slang term for that position.

TAMP BALLAST—Shoring up and leveling track by forcing ballast under the ties, usually with a shovel and a pry rod.

TARGET—A colored blade, often with a lantern attached. The target was attached to a switch stand, and revolved to display a different color according to the direction that the turnout was set.

TELESCOPED—The tendency of railroad cars in a collision to crush through one another, overlapping like the sections of a telescope.

TENDER—The trailing segment of the engine. The tender was an integral part of a steam engine, and was detached only when in the shop for repairs or maintenance. The tender consisted of two bunkers—one for fuel and the other for water. Also called the "tank."

TEN-WHEELER—A steam locomotive with four small pilot wheels on the front, followed by six larger driving wheels. Ten-Wheelers generally were used in passenger service or on fast freights in the late nineteenth century.

THROTTLE—The lever used to control the amount of steam passing from the boiler to the cylinders. The throttle was mounted horizontally on the boiler backhead, and was adjusted by the engineer's left hand.

TIME FREIGHT—A freight train that carried a perishable or important commodity. A time freight was given priority over other freights in order to adhere to a close schedule, much the same as a passenger train. Time freights usually made only a few scheduled stops between division points, most often to take on water or coal.

TISSUE—See "flimsy."

TORPEDO—A small, noise emitting explosive device that was strapped to the railhead. The torpedo exploded with a loud report when run over, thus warning the engine crew of a danger ahead.

TRACKWALKER—A track inspector who carried tools to make on-the-spot repairs to such things as loose bolts and spikes.

TRAIN BUTCHER—A boy who sold newspapers, magazines, dime novels, and candy aboard a passenger train.

TRAIN ORDERS—The written instructions to a train crew, telling them such things as where to take a siding, where to meet another train, and when to leave or arrive at a given point. Generally, train orders covered contingencies that were not specified in a published timetable. The most common train order, the Form 19, was written on thin, onion-skin paper and passed to the engineer and conductor via a small, wooden hoop that was snagged by the crewmen. Hence the term, "hooping up orders."

TRAIN ORDER STATION—A station designated to copy orders from the dispatcher and convey them to a passing train. Not every station was a train order station.

TRAIN (REGISTER) SHEET—A ledger list of all the trains running in a given territory over time. The dispatcher used the sheet to keep tabs on the trains in his division, as did some agent-operators.

TRIPLE VALVE—An air brake pressure regulating device located under each car.

TRUCK—The wheel and suspension assembly under each end of a car. Most freight cars had four-wheel, two-axle trucks, while some heavyweight passenger cars sported six-wheel, three-axle trucks.

TURNTABLE—Sometimes referred to as the "table," the turntable was a revolving platform located in the center of a roundhouse facility.

The turntable moved in a circular motion to line up with tracks running into the several engine stalls of the roundhouse. With an engine sitting upon it, the turntable could revolve around and completely reverse the direction that the engine faced. It could also line up with tracks that led away from the roundhouse and into the adjoining yard area, thus pointing an engine to an outbound track.

UP IN THE AIR—1.) Slang for moving fast; 2.) Extremely excited.

VAN—See "caboose."

VAPOR CLOCK—One of several slang terms for the steam pressure gauge. At the time of our stories, 200 pounds per square inch of steam pressure was typical of most large engines.

WASH OUT SIGNAL—A lantern or hand signal calling for an emergency stop.

WEDGE PLOW—A large point-bladed snowplow that was pushed ahead of an engine.

WESTINGHOUSE—George Westinghouse, Jr. (1846-1914), the inventor of the railroad airbrake.

WILDCAT (ENGINE)—See "light engine."

WIPER—A roundhouse employee who wiped down an engine after its run.

Y—A three-pronged track arrangement that allowed an engine or short train to back down one leg and pull forward on the other, thus reversing its direction.

YARD LIMIT—An area in which certain mainline running rules did not apply. For instance, inside a yard limit area it was not necessary to send out a flagman to protect the front and rear of a train when the train was stopped.

YEGG—A hobo thief or criminal.

ABOUT THE AUTHOR

As a boy, author Michael Gillespie was mesmerized by the steam trains that daily crested the hill behind his home near Independence, Missouri. He never got over that fascination.

While in high school, Mike "volunteered" to assist the agent at the local depot and while in college he worked for Amtrak in Kansas City's massive Union Station. He would later write about both adventures in articles for *Classic Trains* magazine.

A high school history teacher-turned-writer, Mike began collecting long-forgotten stories of railroad lore as a means of learning more about the history of the railways.

As his wife and kids well know, a Sunday drive with Mike almost always leads to the banks of the Missouri River or to a roadway that runs parallel to a railroad.

Publisher's note:

Michael's interest in railroad history coincides with his studies of river steamboat history. He has written two books on that subject and served for a year as the onboard historian for the steamboat *American Queen*.

Mike Gillespie's first book, *Wild River, Wooden Boats,* has been described as "one of the very best steamboating histories available for the Missouri River." His second book is the highly popular *Come Hell or High Water,* a lively history of steamboting on the Mississippi River and Ohio River.

Both provide entertaining reading and copious collections of historic photographs, charts, and sketches. Both are still in print and available from Great River Publishing, libraries, and better bookstores nationwide.

Visit www.greatriver.com to purchase online. We are very proud to have published Michael's first three books of transportation history. Volumes 2 and 3 of *Old Time Railroad Stories* are currently in process of publication.

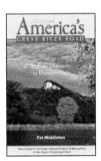   

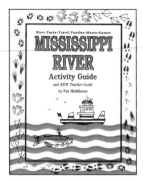

The Mississippi River Activity Guide for Kids

With teacher notes . . . . $19.95 each

by Pat Middleton

Watch the river come alive for your children or students as they

- learn how locks and dams work
- find their way through a maze of river sloughs;
- create a river map;
- identify leaves, plants, animals, and fish along the river.

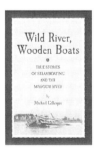 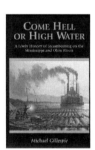 

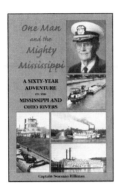

One Man and the Mighty Mississippi
By Norman Hillman

From 1936, when he was hired right out of high school as a deckhand on the towboat *Robert R*, until he retired in 1996, Norman Hillman traveled the waters of the Mississippi River (both Lower and Upper), the beautiful Ohio, the Cumberland, Tennessee, Illinois, Illinois Waterway and the now-abandoned Hennepin Canal. *$23.95*

The River Companion
by Karen "Toots" Maloy

An excellent primer for first-time boaters on the great river. *$9.95*

River Excursion Photo Note Cards

5" x 7" real photo note cards in a variety of Birding, Heritage and River Travel subjects. Individually packaged in clear acetate sleeves. See at www.greatriver.com . . . . *$3.95 each*

Hand-Painted Historic Maps of the Mississippi and Missouri Rivers, the Old Northwest, and More

Map prints . . . . *$24.99 each*

See all maps at www.greatriverarts.com

To order any of our products,
call Great River Publishing toll-free at
888-255-7726
or order securely online at
www.greatriver.com/order.htm

You may also order any of our books by mailing your personal
check or money order to

Great River Publishing
W987 Cedar Valley Road
Stoddard, WI 54658

Please include $7 shipping with your order.